Nicholas

Nicholas Donald
Nicholas Donald

Nicholas Donald

CONTENTS

LOOKING INSIDE
BUSY PLACES
DAVID SHARP

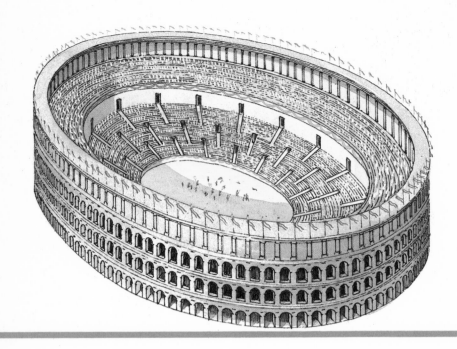

Hampton House

The Parthenon.

The Pont du Gard acqueduct, Nimes

BUILDING FOR GREATNESS

The civilisations of Egypt, Mycenae and later Greece produced architectural wonders of the Ancient World. Their monuments, tombs and public buildings set standards of proportion, space and beauty that architects have had to admire ever since. The powerful grace of the columns that march along the flanks of the Parthenon, even in ruins, instil awe and delight in anyone who will look.

The principles that lie behind the making of structures that will stand against the elements and time itself are better understood now that science has helped the builder by producing systems for calculating weights, stresses and strength of materials. Ancient builders appeared to have had an instinct for what would stand and what would fall; although we only judge by what remains standing, not by what has fallen.

Builders understood at this period — the Parthenon was built around 477-438 BC — ways of supporting a roof on pillars. The system is generally called a post and lintel structure — the lintel being the crosspiece. The delicacy of judgement Ancient Greek craftsmen brought to the technique raised this simple system to the realm of high art. They carved their pillars fractionally thicker at the centre than at the extremities to make them more springy and supple in appearance.

The post and lintel technique was one that was natural to craftsmen in wood and was transferable to masonry. The lintel was secured to the posts by means of pegs projecting from the top of the posts and slotting into holes in the lintels.

Another gifted people, the Etruscans, corbelled the rooves of their buildings. The corbel technique worked gradually inwards from the walls to the apex of the roof to achieve a vault. Greeks brought their gift for geometry to the idea, and taught the Etruscans the use of wedge-shaped stones for the purpose. The simple vault looked rather like an old-fashioned bee hive, and evolved into the arch. With this invention came a new way of spanning spaces with heavy masonry. The Romans were intrigued by the arch, opening a possibility of engineering in the grand style. Their engineers needed a technique of this kind for bridge and aquaduct building, and their architects sought ways of making massive public structures that would celebrate the style and permanence of the grandeur that was Rome, greatest empire of its time.

Post and lintel and the rounded Roman arch persisted as the basis of building styles in Europe well into the Christian era. Public buildings up to the Middle Ages — mostly churches — were post and lintel structures with barrel vaulted roofs *and*, in rare instances, domes. The barrel vaulted roof—rather like an extended round arch — of the church of Conan, Ireland, built around 1080, with its pillars sweeping along each side, has the strength and simplicity of the style called after the Roman source, Romanesque.

Builders began to search for ways of constructing walls with larger and more numerous openings. They had to contend with the great weight of the stone, but wanted larger windows and a more springy style than the fortress-like solidity of the Romanesque style. The use of vaulting whose ribs crossed at right-angles to meet in a point at the centre lent a lightness to the massive stonework and reflected the aspiring spirit of northern thought at this period. The style that emerged is now called gothic. It is characterised by the pointed arch with fan vaulting — seen in Lincoln Cathedral, — slender columns and much increased window space. These soaring spaces were made possible by the way the vaulting distributed the weight of the roof and by the way in which the walls were butressed. The weight of the roof tended to force the walls outwards. This stress was transmitted through the butresses to the solid masonry at the base. The height of this style is seen in the decorated vaults and flying butresses of St George's Chapel, Windsor.

The adapting of materials new to building during the late nineteenth and early twentieth centuries led to some new techniques. In cities where the cost of land was high, people began to build taller buildings. In the USA, steel girders were made into box-shaped structures, one on top of another, to build skyscrapers. The principle of making a framework and filling in the spaces was not new, although its vertical application was. Frame buildings had been in use for hundreds of years. The stave churches of Norway, medieval peasants' huts in Britain and the beautiful Japanese frame houses are a few examples.

The skyscraper use of a frame of steel added new dimensions of strength, and the use of industrialised building techniques involving prefabricated elements in the building increased the speed of the building operation. The Seagram building of soaring glass and bronze, hanging from its inner frame of steel shows how this technique can look when worked with the imagination and skill of great architects.

The box girder structure is really an extension of the post and lintel principle. Little new has been added to the underlying principles of the structure of buildings since the development of the vault and arch. The only new fundamental principle is that of the geodesic dome developed by Buckminster Fuller in the 1950s and 60s. It consists of a series of triangular or polygonal frames attached to one another to make a dome. Unlike other domes, it can be set on the ground without distributing its stresses through walls or pillars. This is the only new principle of building structure to be developed since the late Roman period.

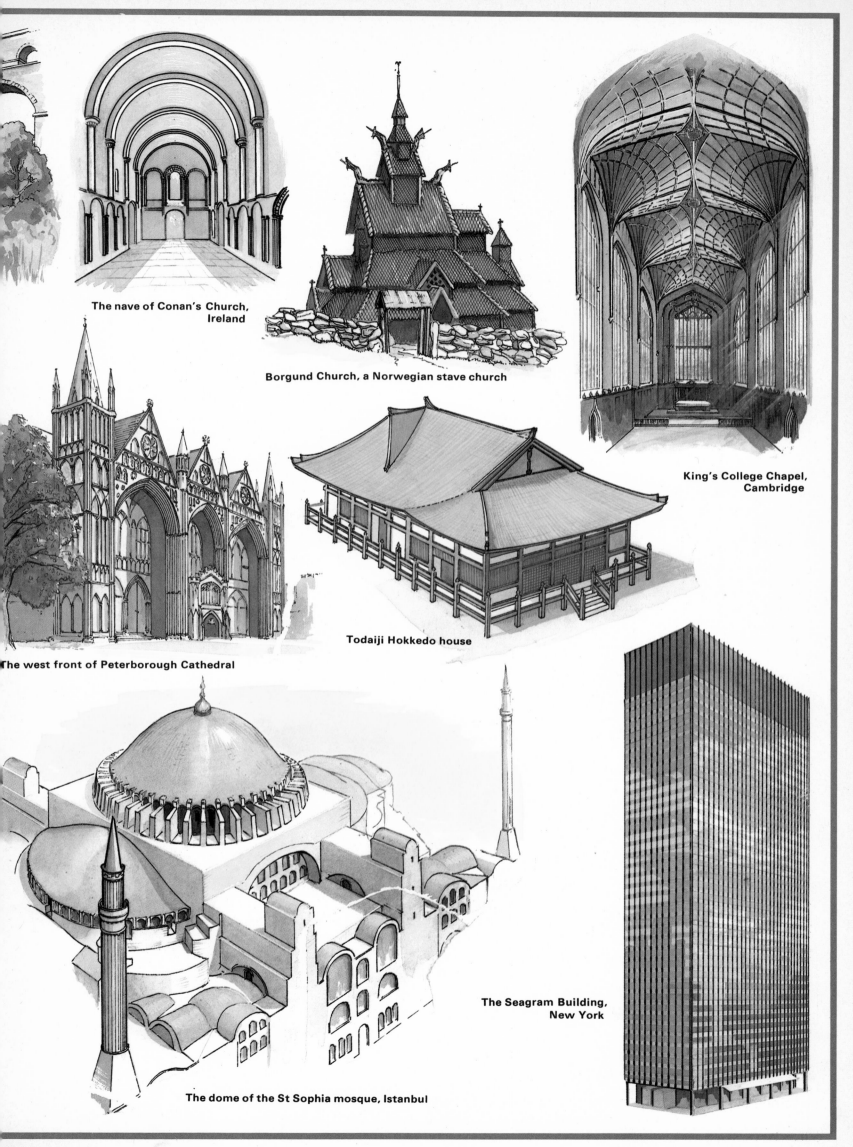

The nave of Conan's Church, Ireland

Borgund Church, a Norwegian stave church

King's College Chapel, Cambridge

The west front of Peterborough Cathedral

Todaiji Hokkedo house

The dome of the St Sophia mosque, Istanbul

The Seagram Building, New York

Stronghold: MEDIEVAL CASTLE

A great administrative and defensive centre of feudal society, the medieval castle stood like a symbol of a baron's power over the lives of his minions and his responsibility to them. In peace he dominated the surrounding country, sallying out to organise his serfs and tenants, gather taxes, to hunt and capture anyone who defied his authority. When attacked, the castle became a safe refuge for his people while he fought outside the walls. If he was outnumbered, he withdrew to the safety of the walls.

The principle of concentric defence was an old one, known since prehistory, when great earth walls encircled a tribal stronghold such as the one at Maiden Castle in Dorset. The idea was that if one defence was overwhelmed, the defenders withdrew to the next ring of defences. Defenders of a medieval castle cleared an area around it to give a good field of fire for their bowmen. The moat was crossed by bridges that were either raised or destroyed before the enemy could cross to the outer bailey. This first wall had turrets from which a good crossfire raked attackers as they climbed the wall. If they broke through this defence, in many castles there was yet another wall — an inner bailey — to scale under fire before they reached the keep. The keep was the heart of the castle and its most strongly defended part. Its garrison could survive a long siege because only a few trained men were needed to defend it. They had a well inside the keep with large storerooms of food and weapons to sustain them.

It was a rare thing for a castle to fall to an assault. More usually the garrison was starved out after a long and expensive siege, or they were betrayed by one of their own people.

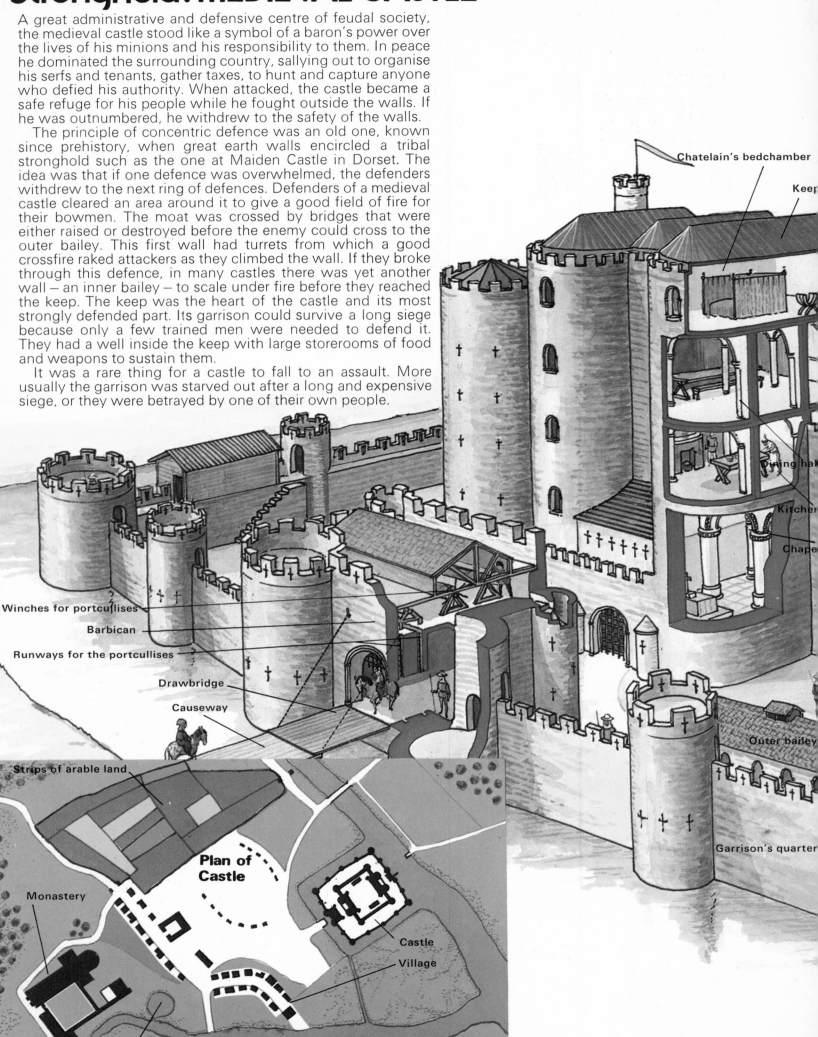

Chatelain's bedchamber

Keep

Dining hall

Kitchen

Chapel

Outer bailey

Garrison's quarter

Winches for portcullises

Barbican

Runways for the portcullises

Drawbridge

Causeway

Strips of arable land

Plan of Castle

Monastery

Castle

Village

Fishpond

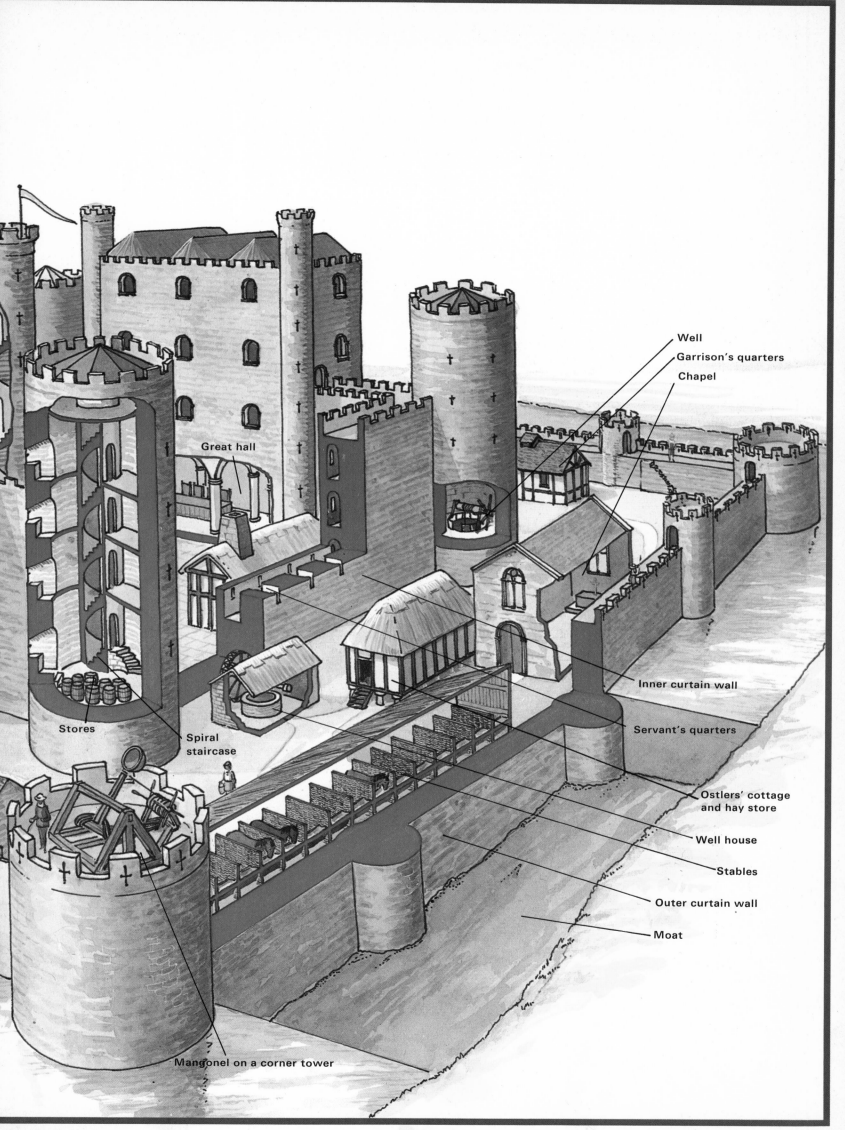

Well

Garrison's quarters

Chapel

Great hall

Inner curtain wall

Servant's quarters

Stores

Spiral
staircase

Ostlers' cottage
and hay store

Well house

Stables

Outer curtain wall

Moat

Mangonel on a corner tower

Monument to immortality: THE GREAT PYRAMID

The greatest stone structure in the world is still, after more than 4,500 years, the Great Pyramid at Giza. Cheops, sometimes called Kufra, Pharoah of Egypt, raised his pyramid on a ridge of rock in the desert about 2680 BC. The building was to act as his tomb and to preserve the conditions and security of his corpse necessary if his *ka* (his spirit double) were to complete its journey to the underworld and send back blessings on his people.

Pyramids may have had other purposes too. They were certainly religious symbols, and some mathematicians believe that they also symbolised a natural and mathematical order. For example, the perimeter of the Great Pyramid divided by twice its height produces 3.144, which is remarkably close to π (3.14159), and there are many other mathematical and astronomical calculations that can be made from the tomb.

The most striking aspect of the building though is its colossal size. It covers an area of about 13 acres (5.25 hectares) and it would be possible to fit four large cathedrals into the pyramid. The organisation of labour that must have been applied to constructing the pyramid was one of the most impressive feats of the ancient world. It took between 20 and 30 years to build, and required approximately 2,300,300 blocks of stone weighing on average 2.5 tons, while some of the massive granite blocks used in the interior of the pyramid weighed much more—up to 4 tons.

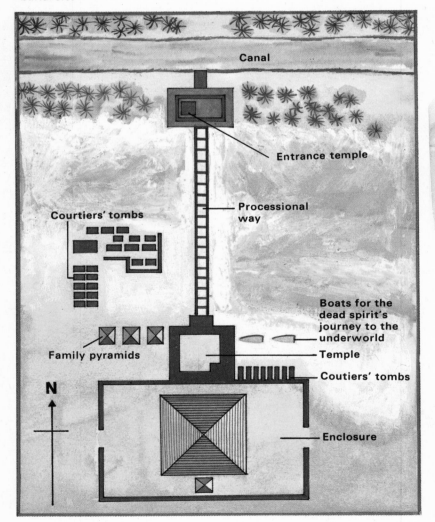

Plan of an Ancient Egyptian burial site

Canal

Entrance temple

Processional way

Courtiers' tombs

Boats for the dead spirit's journey to the underworld

Family pyramids

Temple

Coutiers' tombs

N

Enclosure

Site level

Inner core of yellowish limestone from Jabal al Moquattam

Length of the base is 754 feet 7½ inches (230 metres)

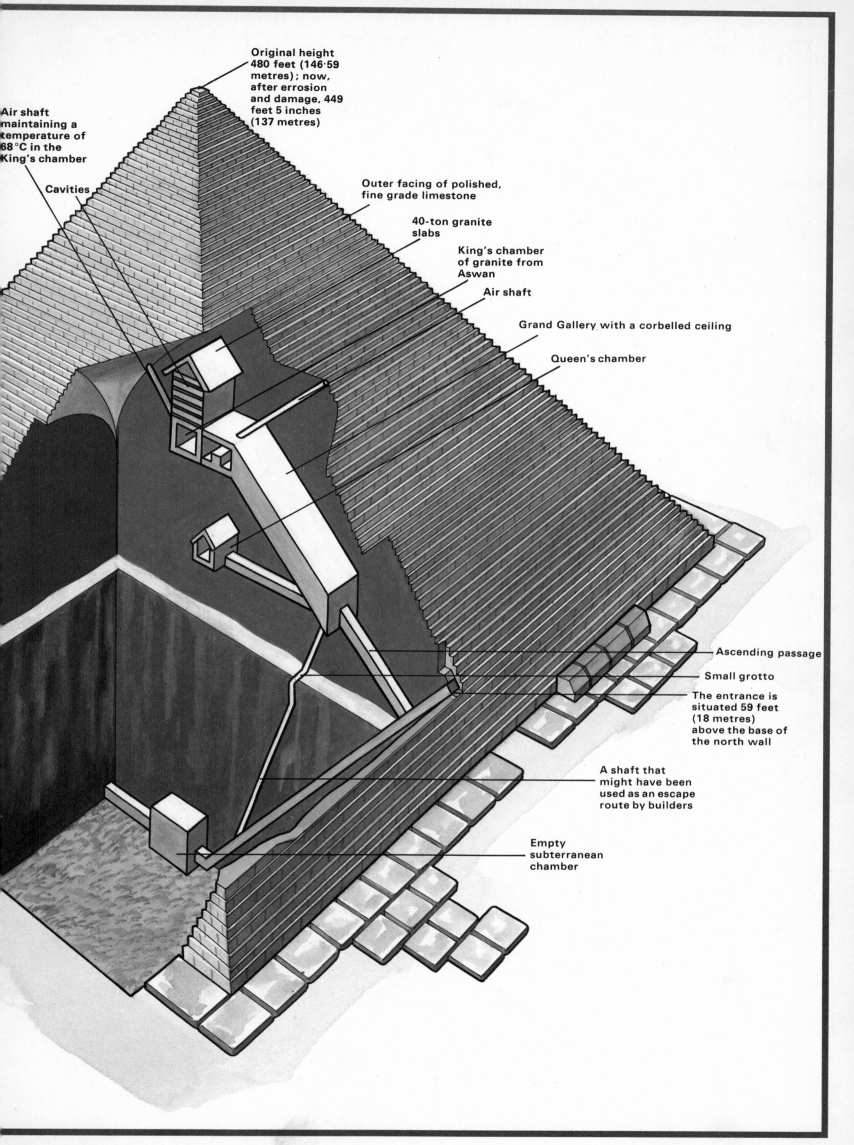

Air shaft maintaining a temperature of 68°C in the King's chamber

Cavities

Original height 480 feet (146·59 metres); now, after errosion and damage, 449 feet 5 inches (137 metres)

Outer facing of polished, fine grade limestone

40-ton granite slabs

King's chamber of granite from Aswan

Air shaft

Grand Gallery with a corbelled ceiling

Queen's chamber

Ascending passage

Small grotto

The entrance is situated 59 feet (18 metres) above the base of the north wall

A shaft that might have been used as an escape route by builders

Empty subterranean chamber

Multi-decked car parks

Elevated departures road

Lower arrivals road

Air terminal building with piers to aircraft and multi-deck car parks

Air conditioning machinery

Licensed bar

Buffet and tea bar

Services duct

Domestic passenger's balcony lounge

Services duct and lifts

Offices

Air-conditioning and ventilation machinery –
hot and cold water systems

Stairs to departure hall

Offices

Bridge connection to pier

Transfer desks

Offices

Passengers'
lavatories

Domestic departures lounge

Bookstall

Public telephones

Airline office

Shopping precinct and display cases

Conveyor belt

Check-in desk

Entrance and exit doors

Departures elevated road

Departures baggage sorting area

Baggage stores and offices

Entrance and exit doors to coach road

Passengers' lavatories

Public telephones

Duty traffic officer's position

Airline counters   Entrance and exit doors   Bank   Information desk

Take-off town: AIR TERMINAL

The world's busiest airport, London's Heathrow terminal offers all the facilities needed by the 15,000,000 people who use it every year. It is like a small town with banks, shops, restaurants, servicing facilities, car parks and even a church. About 40,000 people work to keep the terminal running efficiently day and night.

Around 65 airlines use Heathrow, and each requires complex services. A control tower that has a view from 120 feet (36.58 metres) above the runways, supervises the flow of traffic in the air and on the landing strips. The surrounding buildings — 75 feet (22.86 metres) high' — are built on a diamond-shaped plan. Branching from them are the piers and jetties from which the passengers board the aircraft and onto which they disembark. The roads by which the passengers arrive and depart pass through tunnels, leaving the runways area uncluttered.

The terminal building gives the passengers a comfortable environment in which to wait for their flight or pass through the disembarkation procedures. The staff operate an information system in several languages, security systems to reduce the danger from criminals — especially hi-jackers — medical teams to arrange quarantine and injections for passengers who have been in contact with infectious disease, and emergency teams for fire fighting and first aid. The design of the buildings allows a free flow of passengers so that they have a comfortable walk of less than 1,000 feet (304 metres) to their boarding or baggage collection points. The teak, aluminium, bronze and marble interior of the air-conditioned buildings make them pleasant places in which to work or wait.

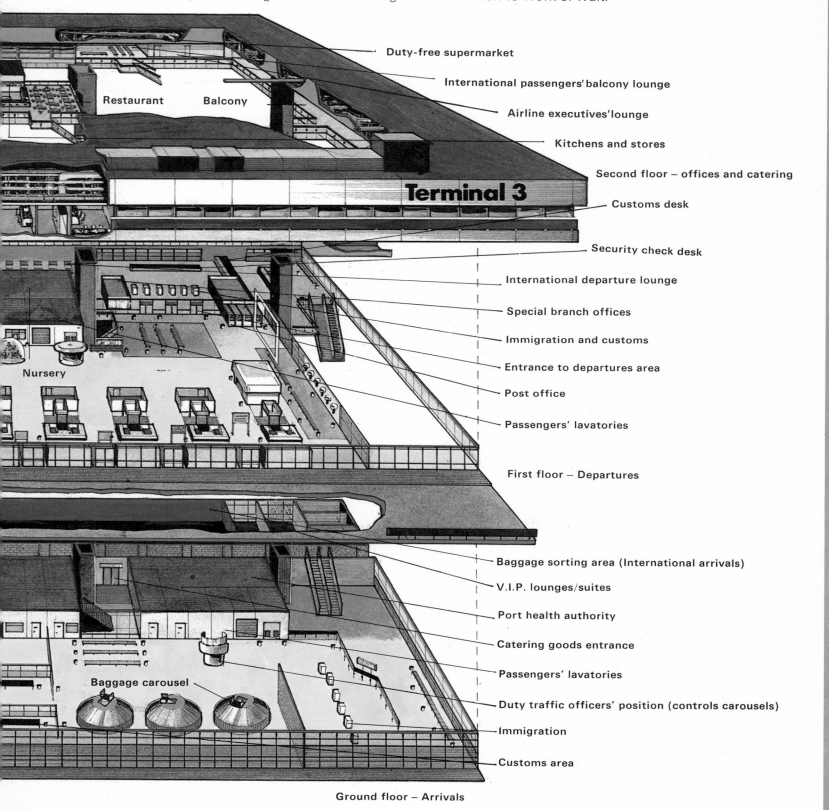

Duty-free supermarket

Restaurant   Balcony

International passengers' balcony lounge

Airline executives' lounge

Kitchens and stores

Second floor — offices and catering

Terminal 3

Customs desk

Security check desk

International departure lounge

Special branch offices

Immigration and customs

Entrance to departures area

Nursery

Post office

Passengers' lavatories

First floor — Departures

Baggage sorting area (International arrivals)

V.I.P. lounges/suites

Port health authority

Catering goods entrance

Passengers' lavatories

Baggage carousel

Duty traffic officers' position (controls carousels)

Immigration

Customs area

Ground floor — Arrivals

A place for people: FAMILY HOUSE

The family house has evolved slowly, with builders and architects making increasingly efficient services for its inhabitants. Within the house, hidden beneath the bricks and plaster, are its life support systems. A great French architect, Le Corbusier, once described a house as a machine for living, and while this may not be immediately obvious, it is certainly true. The modern version of this machine keeps its inhabitants insulated from variations in temperature and from the effects of rain and wind as houses have done throughout history, but it also brings indoors the essential services for comfortable living in a way that was unthought of a hundred years ago.

Waste disposal is no longer a manual chore, involving carrying slops out of the house to a suitable disposal pit. It is enough to pull a plug or flush a lavatory. Fresh water is piped to the house and around it in reliable pipes. The house can be heated without any waste disposal effort, simply by the use of electric, gas or oil central heating systems. The introduction of damp courses, cavity walls and plastics materials has improved the insulation efficiency of houses strikingly.

Here, a typical west European house is opened up for inspection, showing the arrangement of the various systems included in most modern family houses.

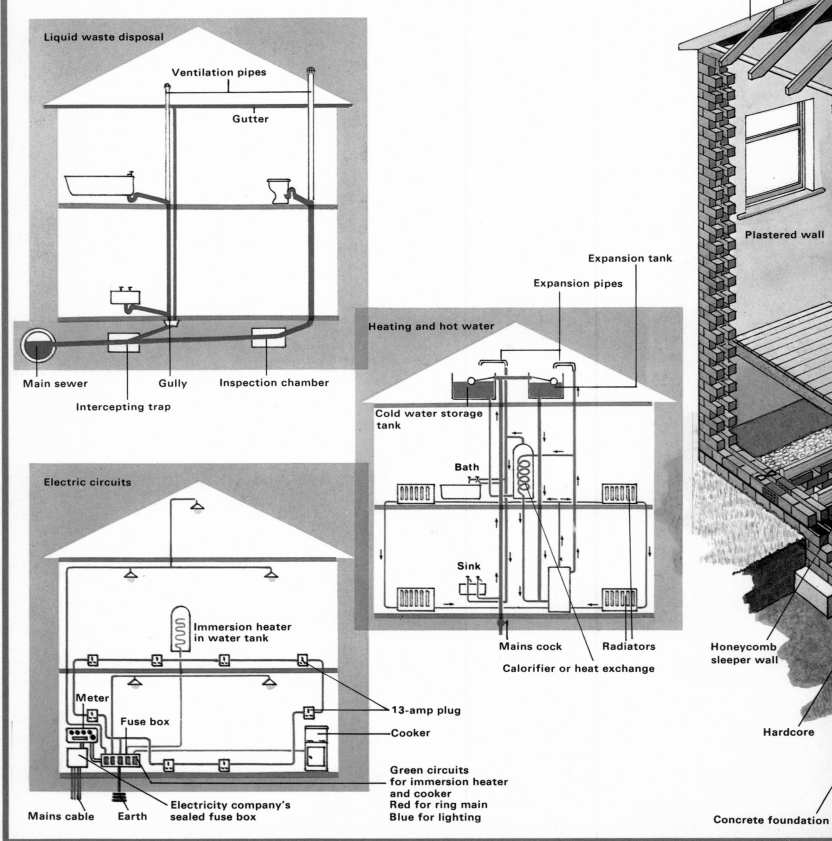

Liquid waste disposal
Ventilation pipes
Gutter
Main sewer
Intercepting trap
Gully
Inspection chamber

Electric circuits
Immersion heater in water tank
Meter
Fuse box
13-amp plug
Cooker
Mains cable
Earth
Electricity company's sealed fuse box
Green circuits for immersion heater and cooker
Red for ring main
Blue for lighting

Heating and hot water
Expansion tank
Expansion pipes
Cold water storage tank
Bath
Sink
Mains cock
Radiators
Calorifier or heat exchange

Hip board
Plastered wall
Honeycomb sleeper wall
Hardcore
Concrete foundation

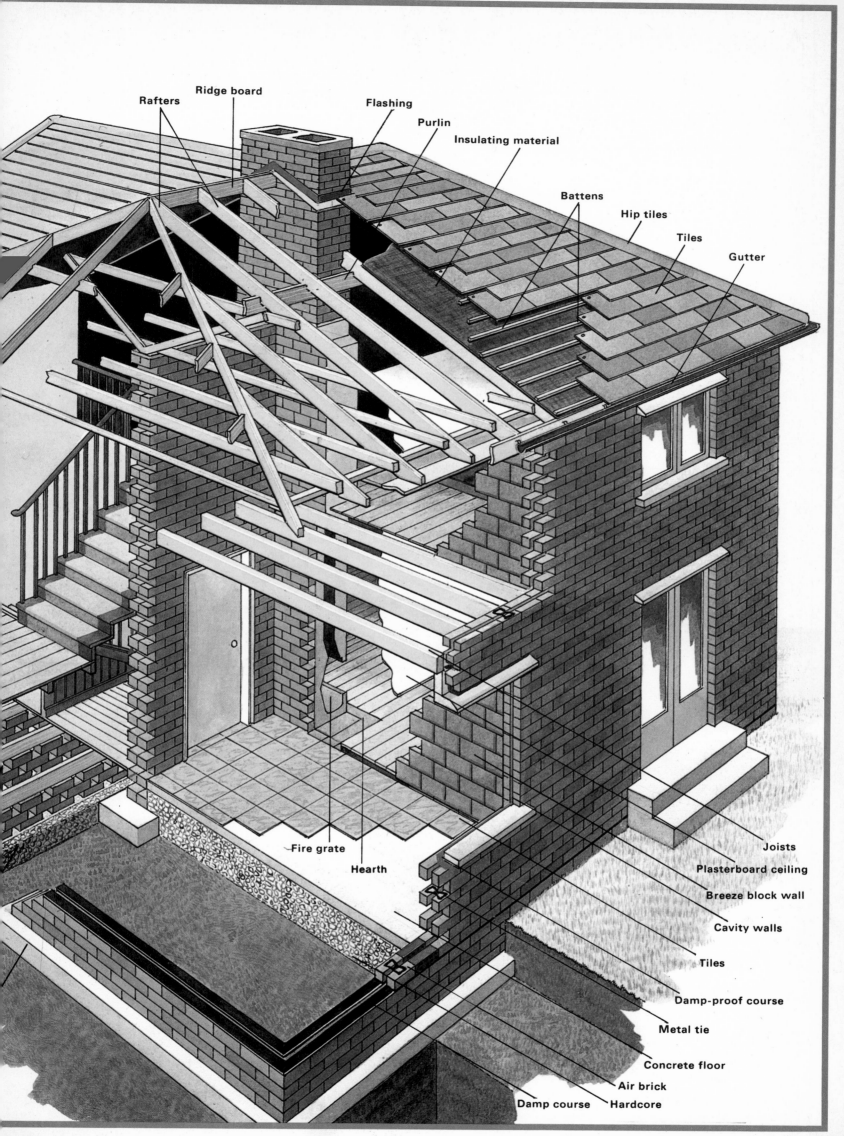

Rafters

Ridge board

Flashing

Purlin

Insulating material

Battens

Hip tiles

Tiles

Gutter

Fire grate

Hearth

Joists

Plasterboard ceiling

Breeze block wall

Cavity walls

Tiles

Damp-proof course

Metal tie

Concrete floor

Air brick

Damp course

Hardcore

Beneath the city: UNDERGROUND STATION

Several short stairways mark the entrance to a modern underground station, but once below ground a traveller may have to find his way through a vast labyrinth of halls, passages, escalators and lifts before he boards his train. The tunnels along which the train moves are cut into the rock with sophisticated boring machines, and then lined with prefabricated steel sections to form a tube through which the rails and electric cables are laid.

At a busy station in the heart of a great city, three lines meet. People walk down stairways into the entrance hall, which has shops and telephones as well as ticket machines and a booking office. They pass through automatic ticket barriers that contain electronic equipment to read a magnetic code on the ticket. The barriers will open only to people who have bought a ticket at the station. Escalators then take the passengers down to the platforms and the trains. Travellers who wish to travel from one line to another follow signs that direct them along inter-connecting passages to other platforms. Most of these interchange routes are designed so that people walk along them in one direction only, and do not have to push past people walking in the other direction. Similarly, people leaving the station travel up escalators that take them to the exit hall, which is situated to one side of the entrance hall, so that they do not meet people hurrying into the station.

Oxford Circus station is one of the busiest in London, but is so well designed that the people who use it rarely suffer inconvenience. Its station master has the use of a closed-circuit television which links him with various parts of the station, and helps him control emergencies when they arise.

Escalators or moving stairs carry people to their trains or up to the street. The treads and the handrail make up an endless belt that is driven round and round by the motor.

Treads

Handrail

Motor

Handrail

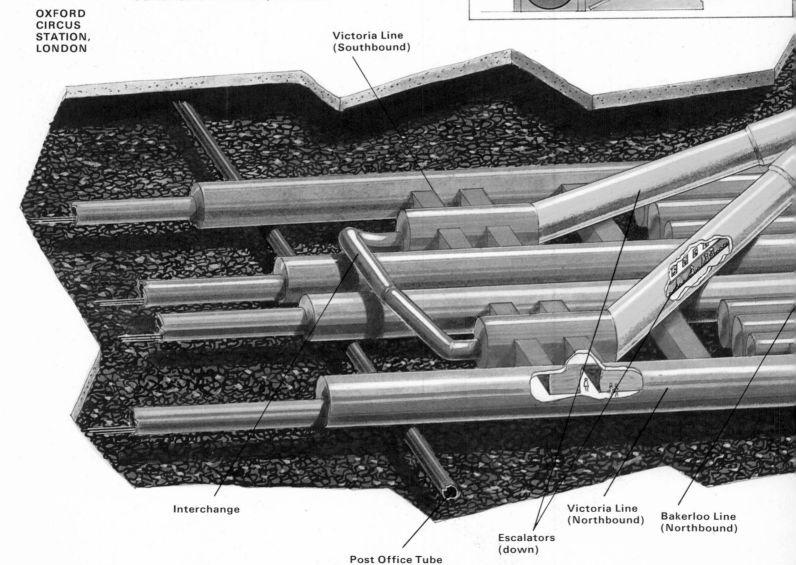

OXFORD CIRCUS STATION, LONDON

Victoria Line (Southbound)

Interchange

Post Office Tube

Victoria Line (Northbound)

Escalators (down)

Bakerloo Line (Northbound)

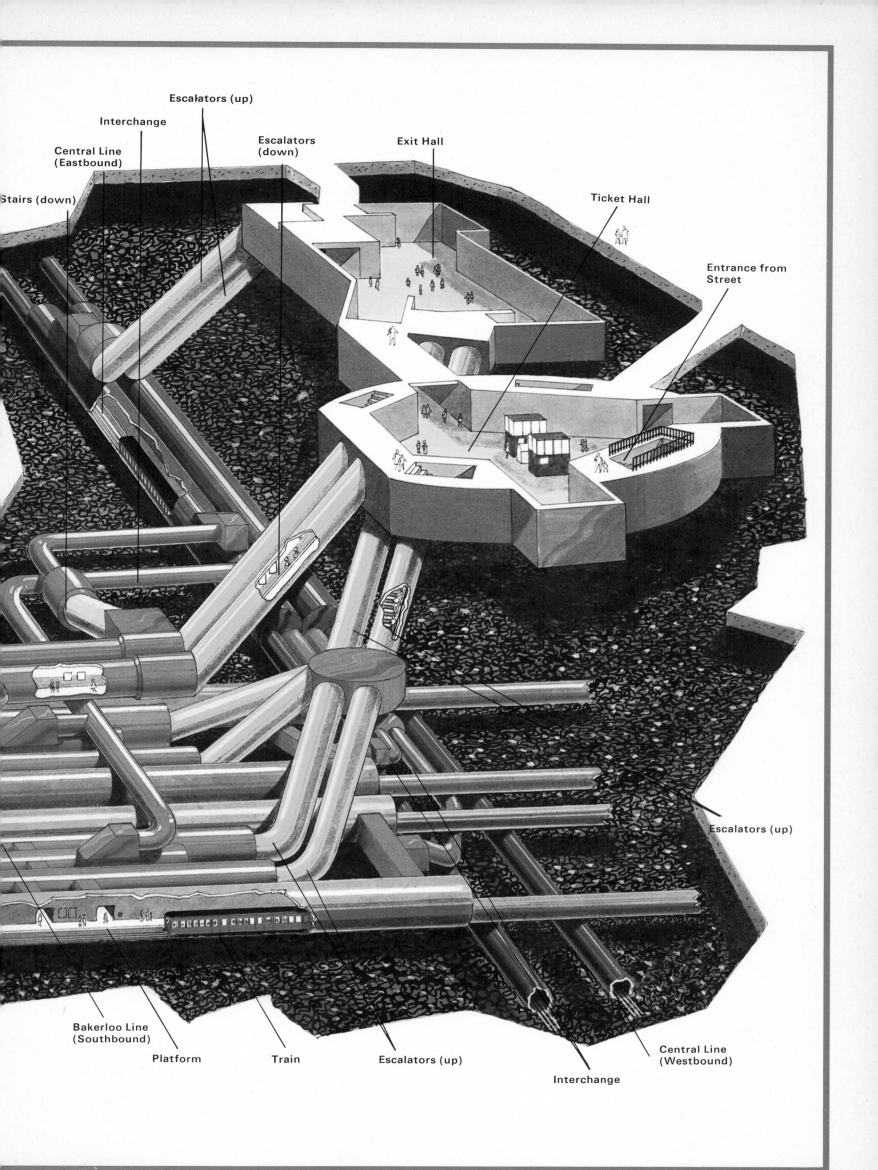

Escalators (up)

Interchange

Central Line
(Eastbound)

Escalators
(down)

Exit Hall

Stairs (down)

Ticket Hall

Entrance from
Street

Escalators (up)

Bakerloo Line
(Southbound)

Platform

Train

Escalators (up)

Central Line
(Westbound)

Interchange

A second home: HOTELS

The modern hotel is a complex structure designed to meet the needs of guests and staff who make a variety of demands on it. There are three main types of hotel, and a great many which are mixtures of these types in various proportions.

There are *transient hotels* that offer accommodation to people who need a room for a brief stay, perhaps just overnight. Many hotels close to transport termini, such as airports or railway stations, are of this kind. *Residential hotels* offer a service to longterm guests who may stay for periods between three months and several years. The guests will require a personal service that makes the hotel a home for them over a long period. Between these two types stands the *resort hotel* for guests who are taking a holiday in a place that has natural attractions or holiday services to offer. The resort hotel is designed to entertain guests for middle-range periods, between a few days and a couple of months. Many hotels of this kind are for a seasonal trade, and may close down in an off-season.

Visitors to a modern hotel will usually enter a foyer where a porter will collect their baggage and arrange for it to be taken to the correct room. In the foyer will be a reception area where guests book in and receive keys to their bedrooms. They will then be shown to their rooms by porters. The hotel will offer them services for eating, the kitchens and dining rooms generally being on or near the ground floor. There will be lounges where guests can relax with a book or talk with other guests. In the foyer there may be a range of small shops selling such things as jewellery, leather goods, toilettries, books and magazines. In the evening, a large hotel may have dances, cabarets and discotheques to entertain its guests. Sun lounges, sauna baths and a swimming pool are commonly found in large resort hotels. Large city hotels frequently have a conference centre where meetings of groups of people will find telephone, secretarial and discussion facilities of an elaborate nature at their disposal.

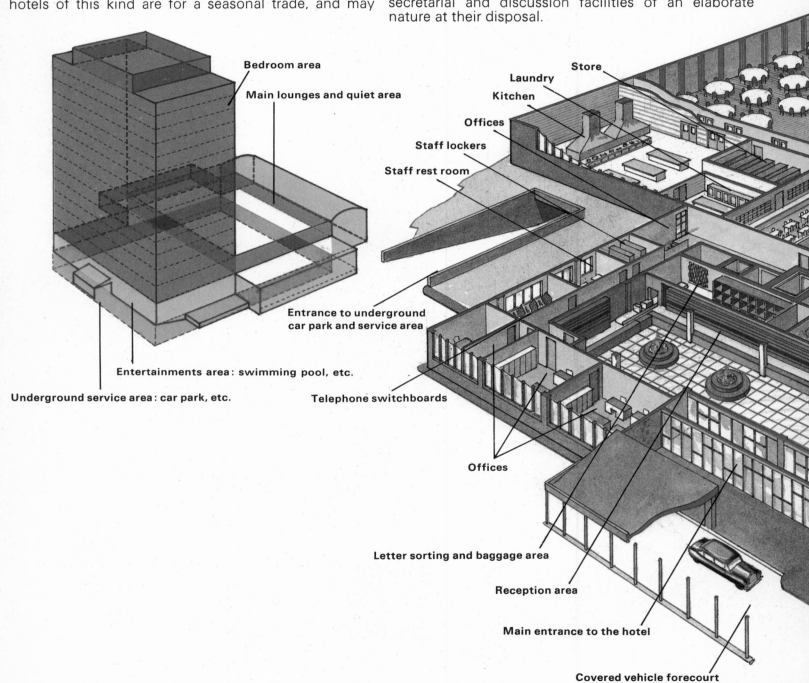

Bedroom area

Main lounges and quiet area

Store

Laundry

Kitchen

Offices

Staff lockers

Staff rest room

Entrance to underground car park and service area

Entertainments area: swimming pool, etc.

Underground service area: car park, etc.

Telephone switchboards

Offices

Letter sorting and baggage area

Reception area

Main entrance to the hotel

Covered vehicle forecourt

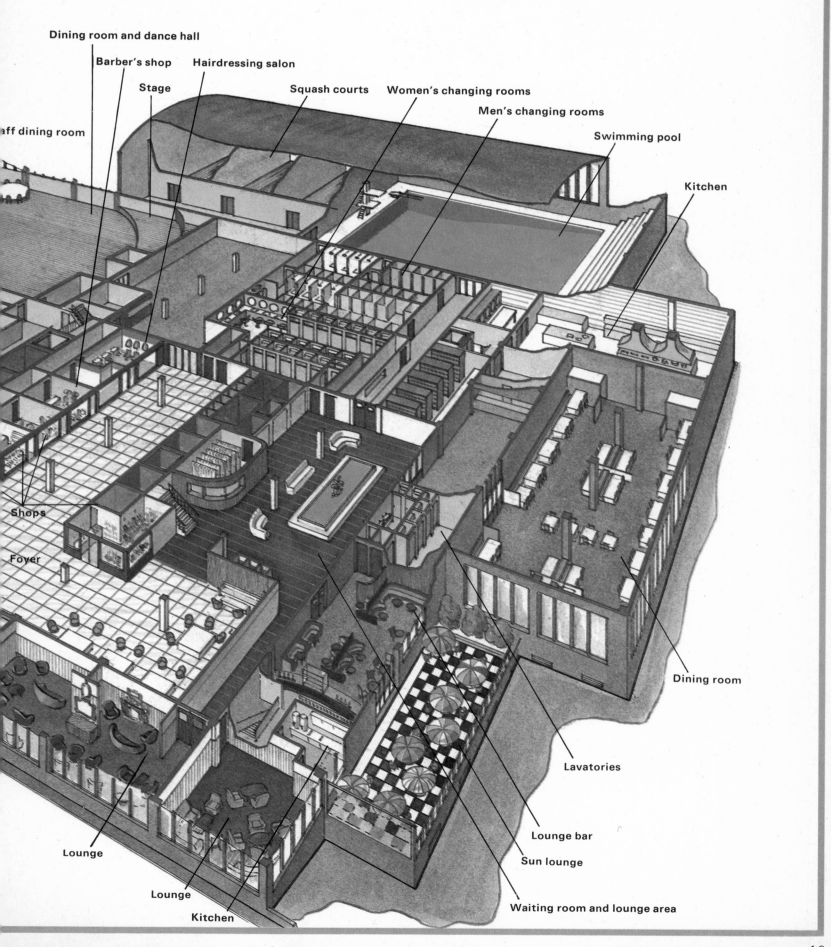

Dining room and dance hall

Barber's shop

Hairdressing salon

Stage

Squash courts

Women's changing rooms

Men's changing rooms

Swimming pool

Staff dining room

Kitchen

Shops

Foyer

Dining room

Lavatories

Lounge

Lounge bar

Sun lounge

Lounge

Waiting room and lounge area

Kitchen

An opencast mine

A farmyard

A juggernaught lorry

BUILDING FOR WORK

About half of your conscious life will be spent working. A Victorian working man, used to long hours at his trade, would rightly have claimed that he spent more like two-thirds of his waking hours working. Some students of working habits maintain that the Victorian worker had only a little less leisure than his modern counterpart. The reason is that a Victorian usually lived within a few minutes walk of his work, while many modern workers spend up to an hour travelling to and fro.

It is clearly important that the places where we spend so much of our lives should work efficiently and be as pleasant as possible. For some types of work, it is easy to provide safe, comfortable surroundings. In a hotel or a shop, the staff should be fairly comfortable most of the time; but some industries are dangerous and dirty, making it extremely difficult to plan pleasant conditions.

It is possible to think of work in five main categories: extraction industries, including mining and deep-sea fishing; manufacturing, which may take place in a factory, craftsman's workshop or even on a farm; distribution, where goods are moved by air, road, rail or sea, warehoused and sorted; selling, which may be done in a shop, market or even an office; and administration, usually performed in an office. Most service industries, such as car service garages and laundries, fall into one of these categories. Entertainment may perhaps be thought of as separate from the others.

The greatest problems arise in designing for the safety and comfort of workers in the extraction industries. How can the coalface of a mine be made a place of comfort and a delight to work in? With the danger of explosive mixtures of coal dust and air, methane gas from the workings, sometimes considerable heat, always a high level of noise from machinery and the worrying thought of the millions of tons of rock hanging over-head, the problem looks insuperable. There is at least one way to overcome it however, that is to take the miners from the most dangerous and unpleasant parts of the pit. This ideal has nearly been achieved in some mines, where miners can operate their machines and conveyers from a safe distance for much of the time.

Opencast workers have other problems. They have to work in all weathers in dirty conditions. Most of them operate machines or drive dumper trucks so, in a sense, these become the surface miner's place of work. Designers and engineers have produced cabs that are warm and well ventilated and with handy controls.

Conditions are at their most harsh in the trawlers of the deep sea fishing fleet. Often in sub-zero temperatures, with the decks heaving beneath their feet, the crews work bitter arduous hours, separated from the comforts of home and family for long periods. Trawlers today are far more comfortable than those from which fishermen of 40 years ago worked. Owners have installed improved radar and wireless equipment so that skippers can receive news of severe storms bearing down on them, and can signal for help when a fisherman is badly injured or the ship is in distress.

It is unlikely that much can be done to improve the best existing conditions for workers in the extraction industries. Farm workers continue to work out of doors in all weathers, but modern tractors with covered cabs, save them from some of the hardships of the life. The use of milking parlours, battery farming of chickens and greatly improved farm buildings make the farm worker's life a much healthier one, though still a rough one.

The greatest strides have been made in improving conditions in factories over the last century. The grimy,

A car production line

An industrial laboratory

A supermarket check-out

An open-plan office

dark, brutalising buildings of the past are now only rarely seen, and even those are much improved. Henry Ford was one of the revolutionaries of the factory. He applied the technique of mass production to the manufacture of cars with such success that other manufacturers adopted the production line system to their own uses. The need for a long line of workers and machines became the dominant requirement of most factories, so builders and architects made long low factories with as few internal walls as possible. This called for an increased use of lightweight, loadbearing materials. Steel and concrete building techniques were still in their infancy at this period, and factory builders did much pioneer work with them.

The new factories are still noisy places generally, but they are lighter, more spacious, and the temperature control is better. National governments make legally binding regulations to which factory owners must comply. If their buildings fall below these standards, inspectors recommend improvements that the law can force the owner to make.

In the 1940s, production planners became excited about the applications of automation. They were so enthusiastic that many people believed that factories would be run with only a tiny fraction of the labour they needed previously. A new era of leisure was prophesied. Automation was not a new idea. For some time machines

had been programmed to operate unattended and to control the quality of their own products. New developments in miniaturisation and computers, pushed the principle a little further. The technique is used to manufacture some foodstuffs and chemicals where there are advantages in maintaining a high standard of hygiene.

Distribution of the products of extractors and manufacturers has changed and still is changing fast. Road and rail handling systems have grown so that haulage companies can move things in great bulk. Juggernaut trucks teem the motorways of the United States and Europe, and freight trains move enormous quantities of material to elaborate loading and unloading depots. Air freight has increased also, but still the best way of moving bulky goods across oceans is by ship.

Huge tankers carrying fuel or chemicals from extraction points to refineries have become common. They make long voyages, and their crews spend little time ashore. Their living quarters, in which they may spend three to four months at a time, are luxurious when compared with those of short-haul cargo ships. Container ships have brought great changes to those ports that handle their cargoes. A few dockers only are needed to handle the gantry cranes used to unload the containers of standardised sizes.

The market place of a century ago has been overtaken by the hypermarket and super-stores of today. In highly organised stores that use only the smallest possible labour force, they sell great quantities of goods, saving on costs.

The dim, airless and cold offices of the beginning of the century are hard to find today. Light, open-plan, central heated spaces have become the planner's ideal. Many people feel exposed and distracted in such an open area so in some offices low partitions are erected to give a little privacy. Even those who would prefer a room of their own would not like to return to the squalor of many of the offices of 70 years ago.

Places of work are now recognised for what they are, a part of our lives that should be made as efficient, safe, pleasing and comfortable as possible.

Sterile for survival: OPERATING THEATRE

There was a time when an operating theatre was the dirtiest place in a hospital. From the days of Joseph Lister at the end of the nineteenth century, hospital planners have been aware of the need to organise surgical units that are as aseptic and conveniently arranged as possible. In 1937, a Frenchman named Jean Wallace designed a circular operating theatre, avoiding the dirt traps that lurk in 90 degree corners. The curved walls were difficult to use effectively when most of the machines — which were generally rectangular — would not fit close to them.

The modern octagonal theatre has no acute angles where bacteria-growing organisms may be trapped, and it is constructed to make an adaptable unit. It is a prefabricated module and can be modified to fit into any hospital, however old their buildings may be.

Patients are taken into the theatre through the anaesthetics room, and any unnecessary clothing and blankets are disposed of before entering the sterile theatre. Used and waste materials from the theatre itself are passed through a double hatch and disposed of, while the temperature and sterile air conditions are maintained through ducts in the ceiling. A separate route is used to return a patient to the wards.

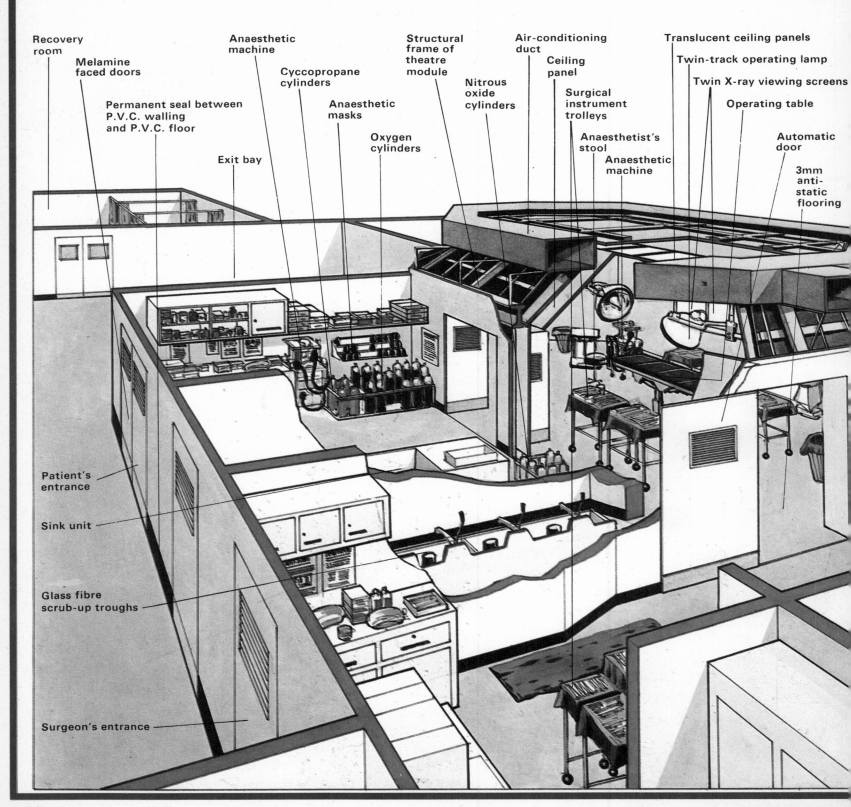

Observation window

Boom arm, supplying many services needed near the operating table

Environment control panel, with controls for: telephone, operating lamps, air-conditioning temperature, and emergency batteries

Recovery room

Melamine faced doors

Permanent seal between P.V.C. walling and P.V.C. floor

Exit bay

Anaesthetic machine

Cyccopropane cylinders

Anaesthetic masks

Oxygen cylinders

Structural frame of theatre module

Nitrous oxide cylinders

Air-conditioning duct

Ceiling panel

Surgical instrument trolleys

Anaesthetist's stool

Anaesthetic machine

Translucent ceiling panels

Twin-track operating lamp

Twin X-ray viewing screens

Operating table

Automatic door

3mm anti-static flooring

Patient's entrance

Sink unit

Glass fibre scrub-up troughs

Surgeon's entrance

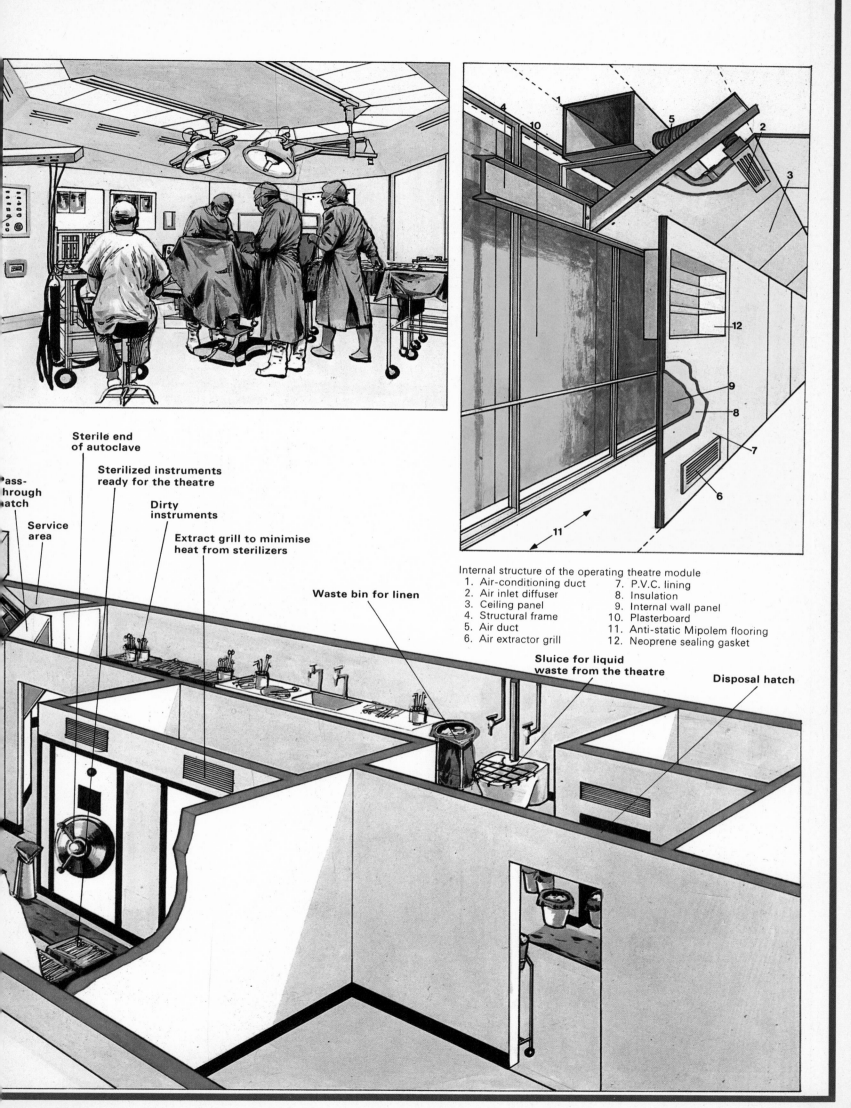

Sterile end
of autoclave

Sterilized instruments
ready for the theatre

Dirty
instruments

Pass-
through
hatch

Service
area

Extract grill to minimise
heat from sterilizers

Waste bin for linen

Internal structure of the operating theatre module
1. Air-conditioning duct
2. Air inlet diffuser
3. Ceiling panel
4. Structural frame
5. Air duct
6. Air extractor grill
7. P.V.C. lining
8. Insulation
9. Internal wall panel
10. Plasterboard
11. Anti-static Mipolem flooring
12. Neoprene sealing gasket

Sluice for liquid
waste from the theatre

Disposal hatch

Furnace and hearth: IRON INTO STEEL

One of the essentials of an industrial society is a plentiful supply of steel for manufacturers of vehicles, other machinery and household appliances. All methods of steel making start with a blast furnace that converts iron ore into liquid iron. In this process, the iron founder feeds ore, coke and other minerals through a double-bell charging system which prevents the hot gases escaping from the furnace. The heat is supplied by the burning coke and gas-heated air, which is blown into the furnace through nozzles called *tuyéres*. Waste material — called *slag* — floats to the top of the molten iron in the hearth of the furnace. The hearth is tapped and the slag drained off, and the molten iron taken to the steel making process.

Steel is refined iron, a process requiring that the steel maker must extract excess carbon, silicon, phosphorus and other minerals from the iron. He can do this by refining it at great heat in one of a variety of furnaces. He may use an oxygen furnace, an electric arc or an open hearth furnace. Open hearth is the oldest technique still in wide use, although in some countries it has been superseded by the faster electric arc furnace.

The open hearth is like a long trough lined with refractory bricks. The operator loads it with scrap iron and limestone and turns up the heat, which is supplied through gas or oil burners. When the scrap is partly melted, he adds molten iron from the blast furnace. He can control the quality of the steel by adding minerals, or speeding the process when necessary by injecting oxygen into the furnace.

When the steel runs off into a ladle, the slag rises to the surface where it can be skimmed off. The molten steel may then be cast into convenient sized ingots, or moulded and run through a rolling mill to form it into sheet steel.

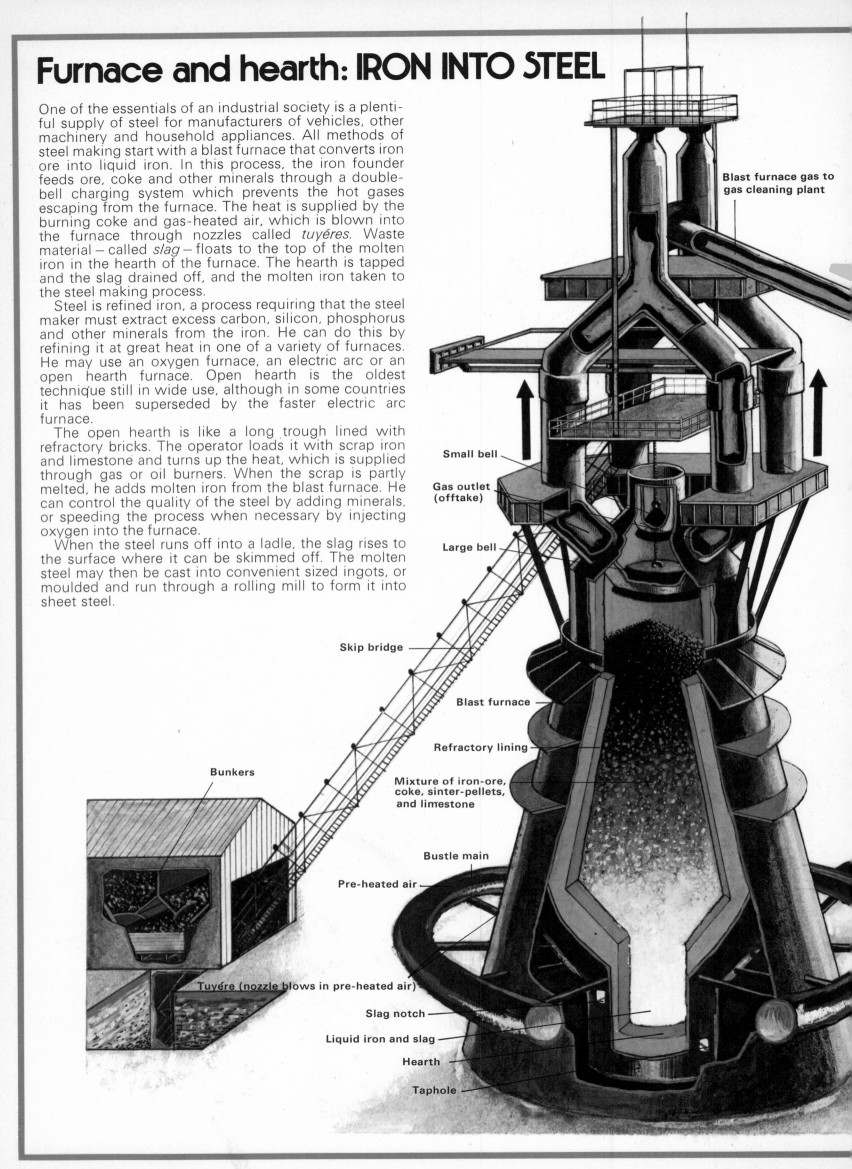

Blast furnace gas to gas cleaning plant

Small bell

Gas outlet (offtake)

Large bell

Skip bridge

Bunkers

Blast furnace

Refractory lining

Mixture of iron-ore, coke, sinter-pellets, and limestone

Bustle main

Pre-heated air

Tuyére (nozzle blows in pre-heated air)

Slag notch

Liquid iron and slag

Hearth

Taphole

Open hearth furnace

Boxes of scrap metal and limestone are tipped by the charging car into the open hearth furnace. The doors are closed and burning gas or oil jets into the material. An injection of oxygen through water-cooled lances speeds up the process, which produces about 350 tons every ten hours.

Downcomer

Blast-furnace gas having passed through dust-catchers and spray chambers goes through gas-cleaning plant to gas-holder

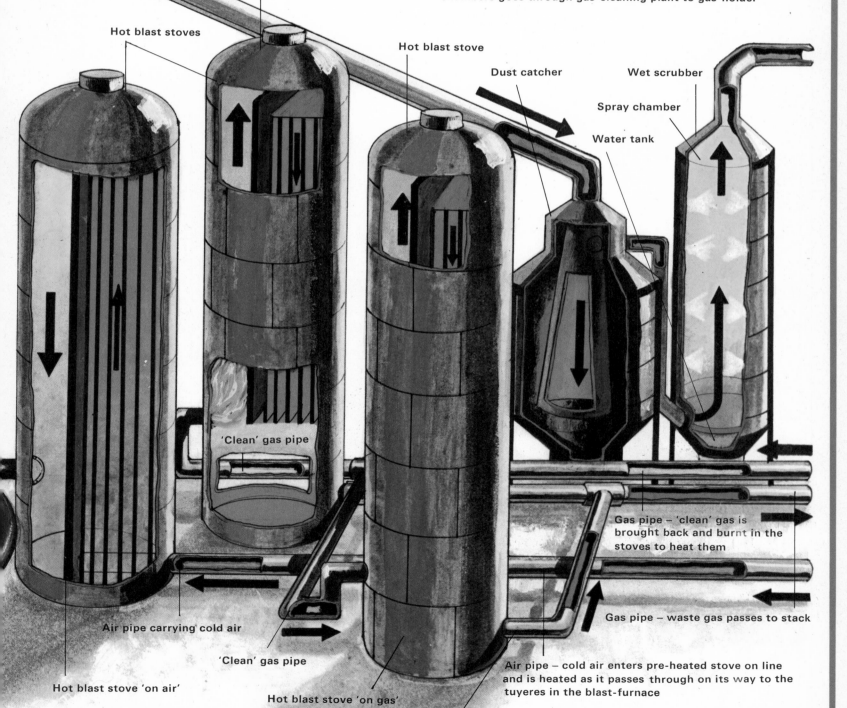

Hot blast stove 'on gas'

Hot blast stoves

Hot blast stove

Dust catcher

Wet scrubber

Spray chamber

Water tank

'Clean' gas pipe

Gas pipe – 'clean' gas is brought back and burnt in the stoves to heat them

Air pipe carrying cold air

'Clean' gas pipe

Gas pipe – waste gas passes to stack

Hot blast stove 'on air'

Hot blast stove 'on gas'

Air pipe – cold air enters pre-heated stove on line and is heated as it passes through on its way to the tuyeres in the blast-furnace

Gas pipe with clean gas for burning in hot blast stove

Putting the wind to work: WINDMILL

From the Middle Ages, windmills became popular in Europe, being used to grind corn, to power pumps and — much later — drive saw mills. In Holland, they held a useful place in assisting the irrigation system, but in the rapidly industrialised countries, such as Germany and Great Britain, machines powered by fossil fuels became more attractive, and windmills became relics of a quieter age. The increasing concern over the world's diminishing fossil fuels in this century have recently drawn technologists' attention to the advantages of power from a clean source for which they pay nothing.

In the United States, small 4-foot (1.22 metres) vaned windmills have been widely used throughout the last hundred years to pump water in country districts. The design of sails has been carefully examined recently so that their efficiency may be improved. Some people believe that small windmills of advanced design offer an answer to the rising cost of electricity. Using windmills of plastic, they harness the wind to turn turbines wired to their domestic electricity supply. In India, planners hope that windmills may have a wider application, replacing the bullock as a power source for turning the machinery of small-scale irrigation systems.

The old, traditional windmill, with its 20 — 40-foot (6 — 12 metre) vanes, produced power of surprising strength, capable of maintaining the grinding action of massive millstones, even in a light breeze.

Sails or sweeps

Millstone arrangement

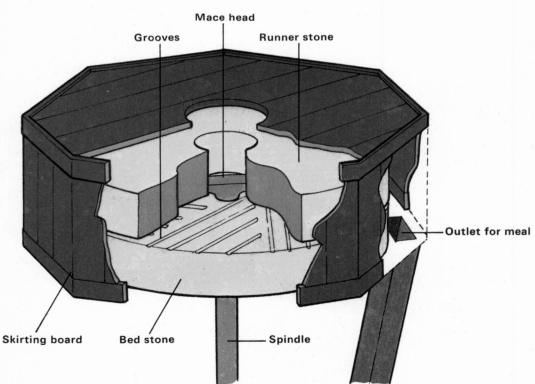

Mace head

Grooves

Runner stone

Outlet for meal

Skirting board   Bed stone   Spindle

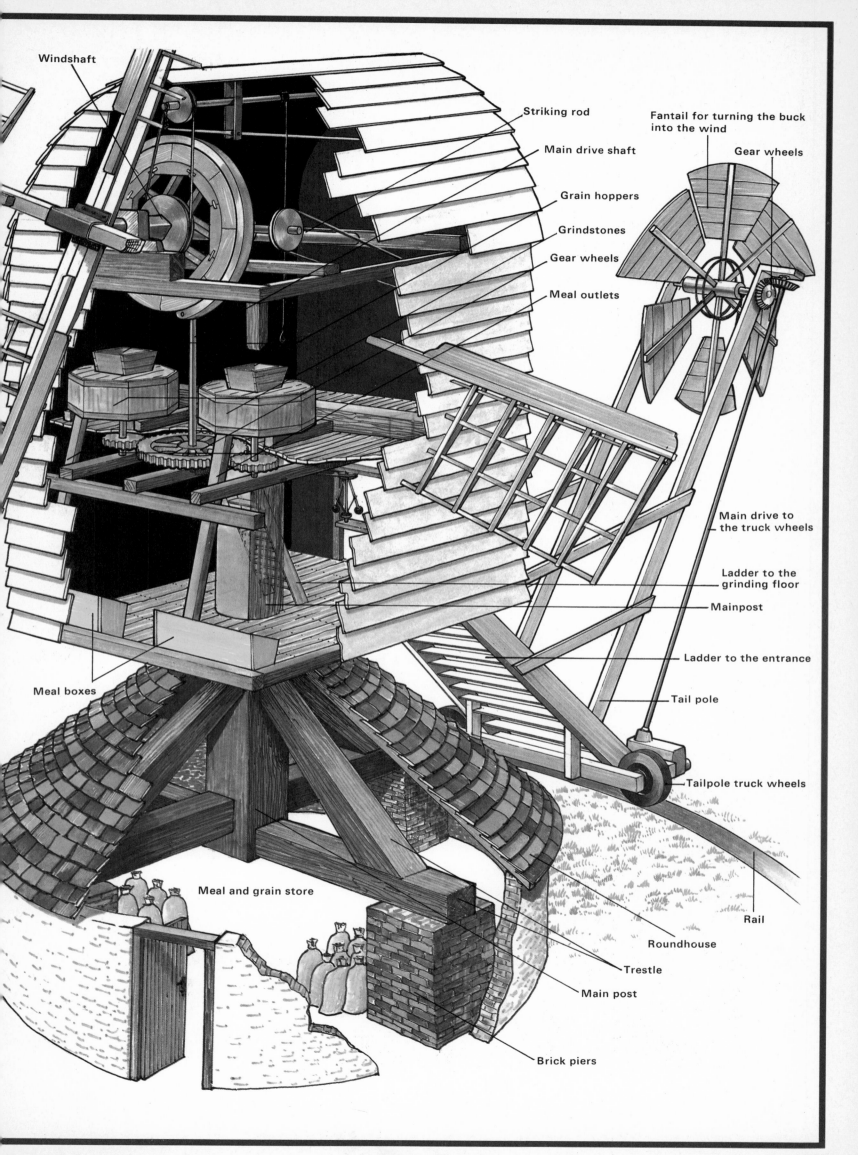

Windshaft

Striking rod

Main drive shaft

Fantail for turning the buck into the wind

Gear wheels

Grain hoppers

Grindstones

Gear wheels

Meal outlets

Main drive to the truck wheels

Ladder to the grinding floor

Mainpost

Ladder to the entrance

Meal boxes

Tail pole

Tailpole truck wheels

Meal and grain store

Rail

Roundhouse

Trestle

Main post

Brick piers

Fossil power: COAL

The most prolific source of fossil fuel in the world is coal. The United States alone has an estimated 3,200,000,000,000 tons of it below ground. With the techniques at present used, only about seven per cent — 217,000,000,000 tons — of that enormous resource can be extracted from the ground.

From the days of the primitive bell pit, techniques of mining have advanced greatly. The bell pit was simply a shaft driven down to a seam. The base of the shaft was enlarged to extract the coal until the roof showed signs of caving in. The mine was then abandoned. Modern methods of dragline mining have speeded up production and reduced costs, but they can generally be applied only to deposits that are fairly near the surface, and these are mostly of bituminous soft coals. The high-grade hard coals are usually found deep in the ground, and for these shaft mining is the only technique known.

Once the shaft is driven to the required depth, the seams of coal can be extracted in various ways. In the United States several mines still use the pillar and stall method. This entails cutting away the coal, leaving wide pillars of coal to support the roof of the mine. For most mines this is a wasteful method of working; but where surface subsidence is a worry and where the seam is fairly near the surface, it may be used.

Many European miners use the longwall system. Using this method, the miners cut galleries to the seam, and then advance into it along its length. They support the roof with moveable pit props (see the inset illustration). As the cutting machines advance, the coal is conveyed along a belt to waiting trucks. The roof behind the props is allowed to collapse in a controlled way as the long wall moves deeper into the seam. The connecting galleries are protected by the use of tube sections and supports.

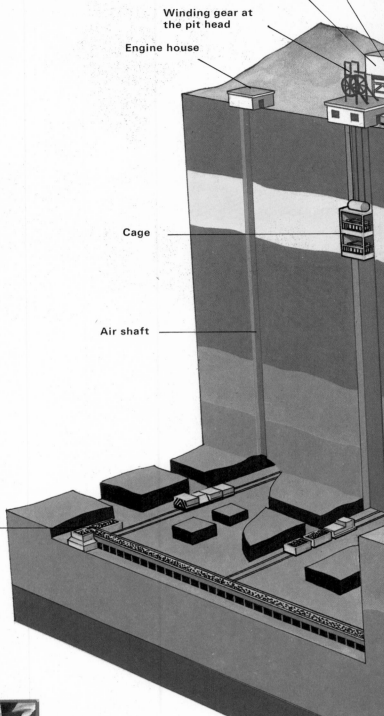

Winding house
Rail head
Winding gear at the pit head
Engine house
Cage
Air shaft
Truck loading point at the end of a conveyer belt

A metal pit prop, working like a car jack, supports the roof. The miner controls the mechanical cutter as it moves along the wall, sending the coal into a conveyer belt and to waiting trucks. As the cutter moves deeper in to the seam, the pit props are moved forward, and the space behind them is filled with rubble to hold up the roof. Only a narrow gallery is left for the coal to pass along and for the miner to use in making his way to and from work.

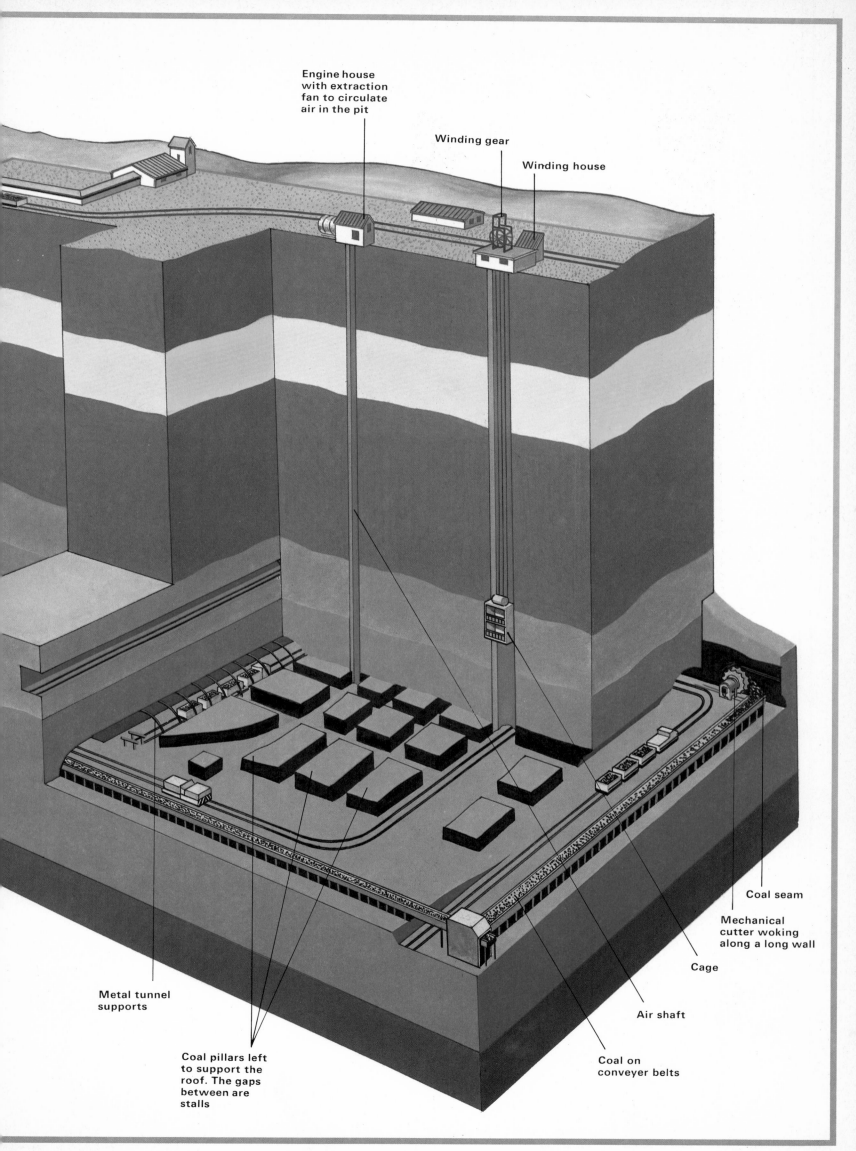

Engine house with extraction fan to circulate air in the pit

Winding gear

Winding house

Coal seam

Mechanical cutter woking along a long wall

Cage

Air shaft

Coal on conveyer belts

Metal tunnel supports

Coal pillars left to support the roof. The gaps between are stalls

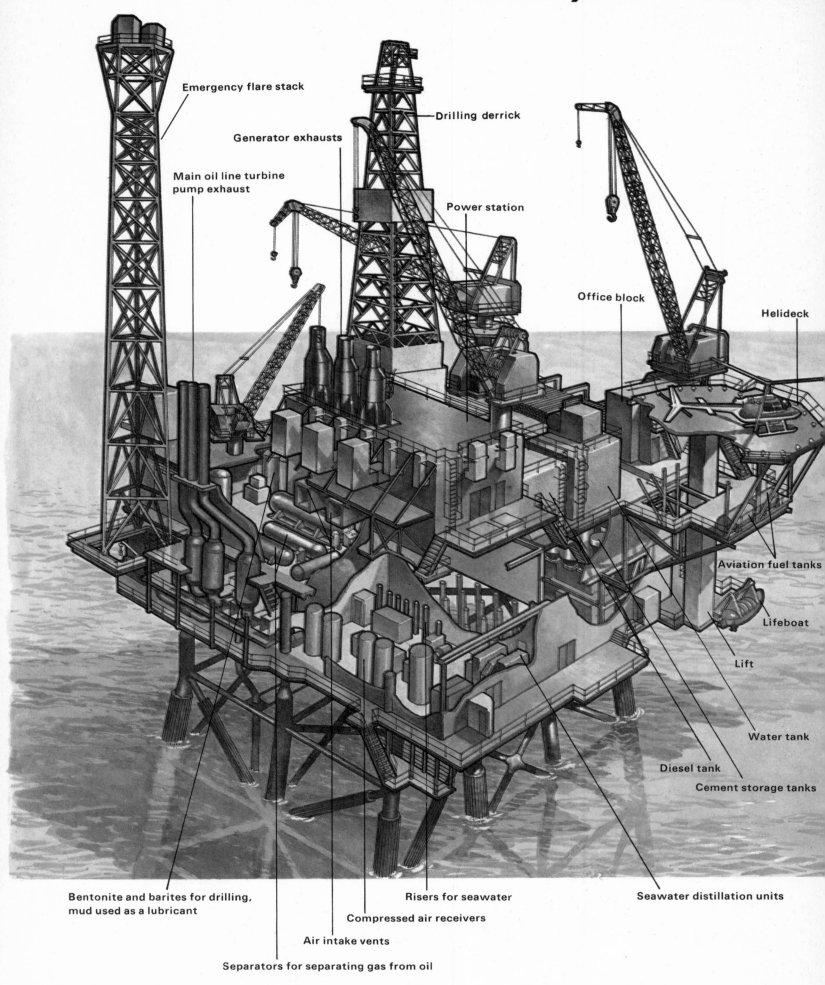

Emergency flare stack

Generator exhausts

Drilling derrick

Main oil line turbine pump exhaust

Power station

Office block

Helideck

Aviation fuel tanks

Lifeboat

Lift

Water tank

Diesel tank

Cement storage tanks

Seawater distillation units

Bentonite and barites for drilling, mud used as a lubricant

Risers for seawater

Compressed air receivers

Air intake vents

Separators for separating gas from oil

OIL DRILLING PLATFORM

Oil men have drilled beneath the ocean for many years, but only since the seventies have they defied the depths and fury of the North Sea. Previously, they sank their wells in shallow water, but in the North Sea they had much greater depths of water and far fiercer weather conditions to struggle with.

This drilling platform stands in the Forties Field. Its legs emerge from the sea bed 420 feet (128 metres) beneath the turbulent surface waves, which can smash up to 80 feet (24 metres) high against the superstructure. The lowest of the three decks comes in for a considerable battering from waves and blown spume in storm winds, because it rises only 77 feet (23.5 metres) above sea level.

The platform is secured to the seabed by its legs, which bite 250 feet (76 metres) into the oceanic crust. The extreme wind pressures, sometimes more than 100 mph (160 kmph), and wave surges acting on the 550 foot (167.6 metres) high structure exert colossal stresses on the *anchors* of the platform.

From the platform, the drills seek out the oil to depths of as much as 11,480 feet (3,480 metres). The drills can be worked at angles of up to 55 degrees so that a great area of the oil-bearing stratum can be penetrated — about 176,785,750 sq ft (17,323,265 sq metres). The 96-man crew, when the platform is producing at full capacity, will pump out 125,000 barrels a day.

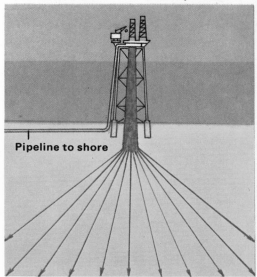

The drills fan out below the platform

Pipeline to shore

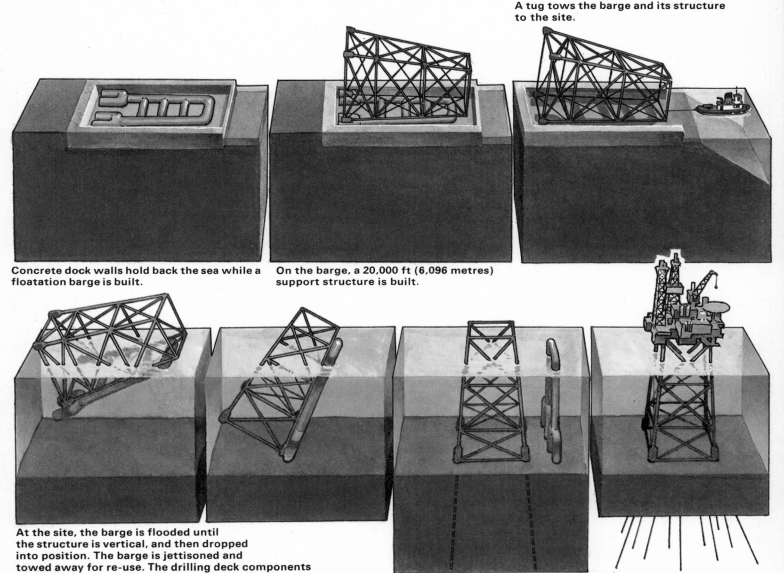

A tug tows the barge and its structure to the site.

Concrete dock walls hold back the sea while a floatation barge is built.

On the barge, a 20,000 ft (6,096 metres) support structure is built.

At the site, the barge is flooded until the structure is vertical, and then dropped into position. The barge is jettisoned and towed away for re-use. The drilling deck components are then assembled so that work can begin.

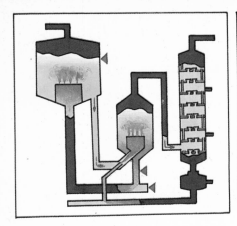

Crude oil is heated in a cracker unit. As the oil is heated it separates into fuels of various grades, the more volatile rising up the column. The grades are tapped from the sides of the unit at the level required for particular grades.

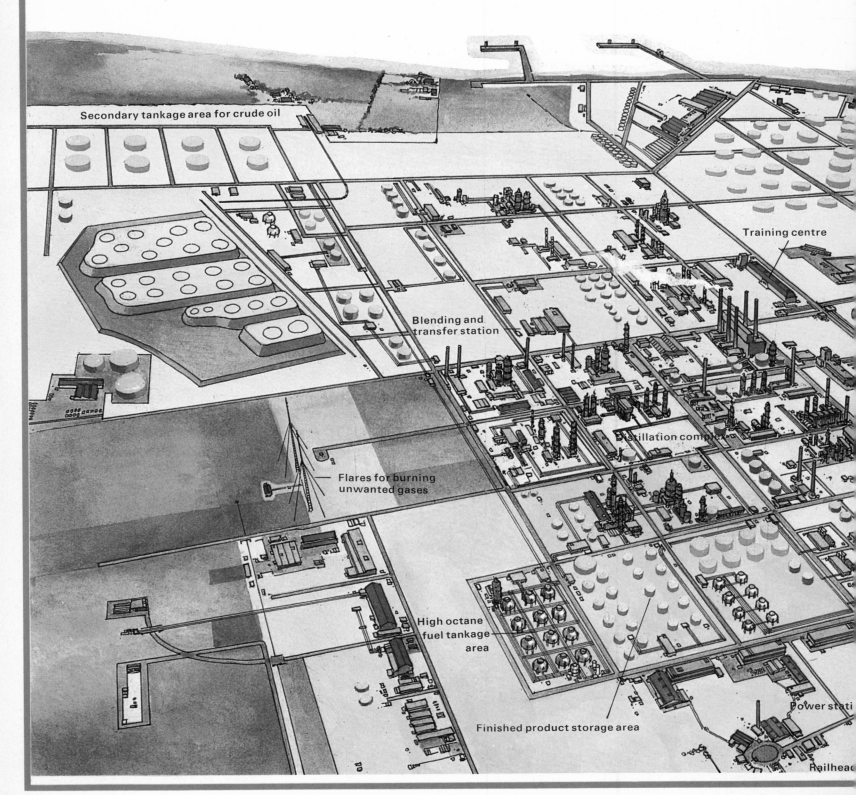

Secondary tankage area for crude oil

Training centre

Blending and transfer station

Flares for burning unwanted gases

Distillation complex

High octane fuel tankage area

Finished product storage area

Power stati

Railhead

Sorting oil's riches: OIL REFINERY

A century ago, oil was taken from its underground home and refined for use in engines as petroleum by distillation. The process was wasteful, because after the petroleum had been extracted, the residues of heavier and lighter oils were usually burned away as unuseable. A few companies, more far sighted than others, pumped back the residues into the wells from which they had been extracted — a practice from which they reaped benefits later when they learned how to use oil's consitituents more fully.

After World War I, the combustion engine developed in numbers, power and diversity of fuel demands at a runaway rate. The oil companies learned to refine the oil more fully than before. This process continued to the present, when researchers continue to learn more about this extraordinary fossil fuel.

The refineries themselves, from their origins as sordid dirty places, have grown into enormous complexes of buildings linked by wide tarmac service roads and gleaming spiders' webs of pipes. The storage tanks are painted silver to reflect light and heat, and there are now many types of distillation units in a refinery so that a great range of products may be extracted from the crude oil.

The crude oil is off-loaded from tankers at the oil terminals and conveyed to storage tanks. As it is required, the oil is pumped to the cracker units where it is heated. Its lighter consitituents are tapped at the upper levels of the unit and the heavier ones lower down. These are further refined in other units and stored until sold. Some are blended in mixer tanks. Many refineries are situated at rail heads, where land transport is effective, and their products can be carried away for use in power stations and industries.

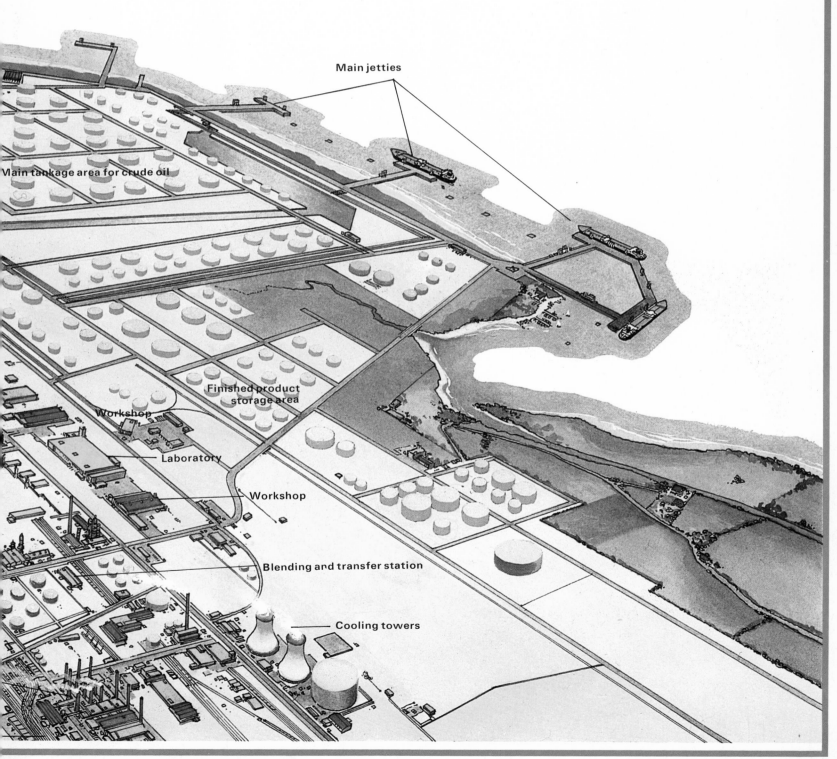

Main jetties

Main tankage area for crude oil

Finished product storage area

Workshop

Laboratory

Workshop

Blending and transfer station

Cooling towers

Fuel for transport: PETROL STATION

When Henry Ford brought in the age of the mass-produced family car, there were few petrol pumps to be found beside the roads. Most of them were in private hands, and were simply hand-operated pumps attached to barrels of fuel. As a barrel was emptied, the pump would be attached to a fresh, full one. Tanks of petrol, sunk into pits in the ground were used by businesses with fleets of vehicles, and the tanks were cleared by fixed pumps.

The early motorists carried with them several cans of petrol if they intended making a long trip. Soon shopkeepers realised they were missing an opportunity of good business, and some would stock a few barrels of fuel with a hand pump for the motorist. Fuel sale signs began to appear more and more frequently along the main roads. One might see the curious sight of a horse-drawn dray stopping to deliver barrels of petrol.

The spread of garages, often growing up on the site of old blacksmiths' shops, came with the increasing numbers of cars on the roads. The garages were usually bound by agreements to sell the product of particular oil companies. The giant tankers delivered their loads to underground tanks which were in sections to accept petrol of various grades. The cost of labour and the huge increase in traffic led to the introduction of self-service garages. Here, the motorist turns a switch on the pump to select the grade of petrol he wants, signals the attendant in the kiosk and fills the tank in the car. The fuel is pumped up from its underground tank electrically, and when the motorist releases the pressure on the trigger of the handpiece, the electric motor is switched off. The amount of fuel is monitored electronically and the cost calculated by a simple computer which registers these facts on a screen so that the attendant knows how much to charge his customer. Using this system, one attendant can deal with customers using several pumps at once.

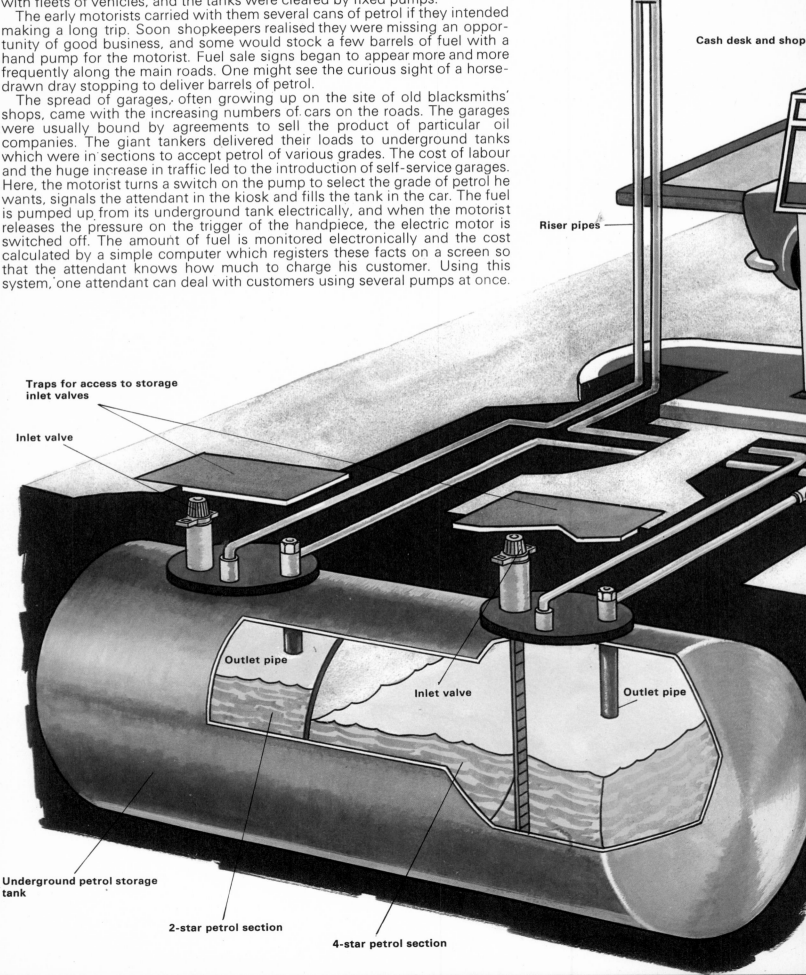

Cash desk and shop

Riser pipes

Traps for access to storage inlet valves

Inlet valve

Outlet pipe

Inlet valve

Outlet pipe

Underground petrol storage tank

2-star petrol section

4-star petrol section

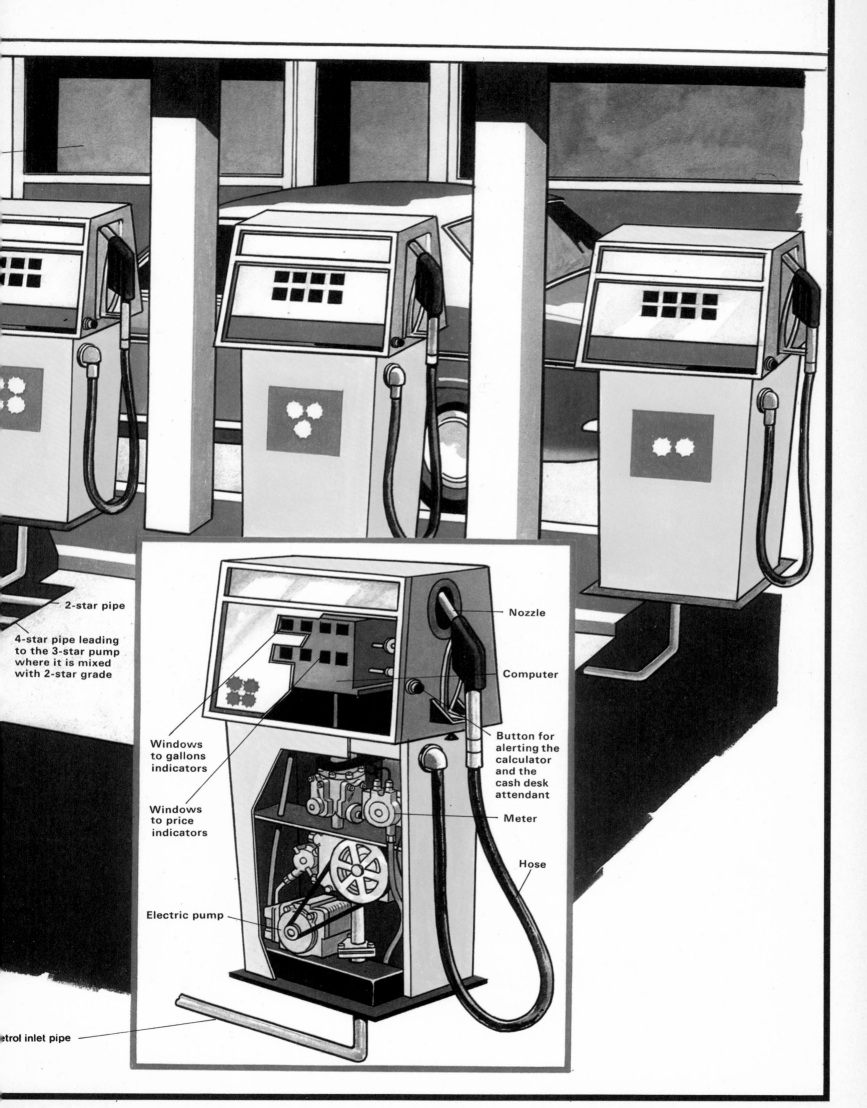

2-star pipe

4-star pipe leading
to the 3-star pump
where it is mixed
with 2-star grade

Windows
to gallons
indicators

Windows
to price
indicators

Electric pump

...trol inlet pipe

Nozzle

Computer

Button for
alerting the
calculator
and the
cash desk
attendant

Meter

Hose

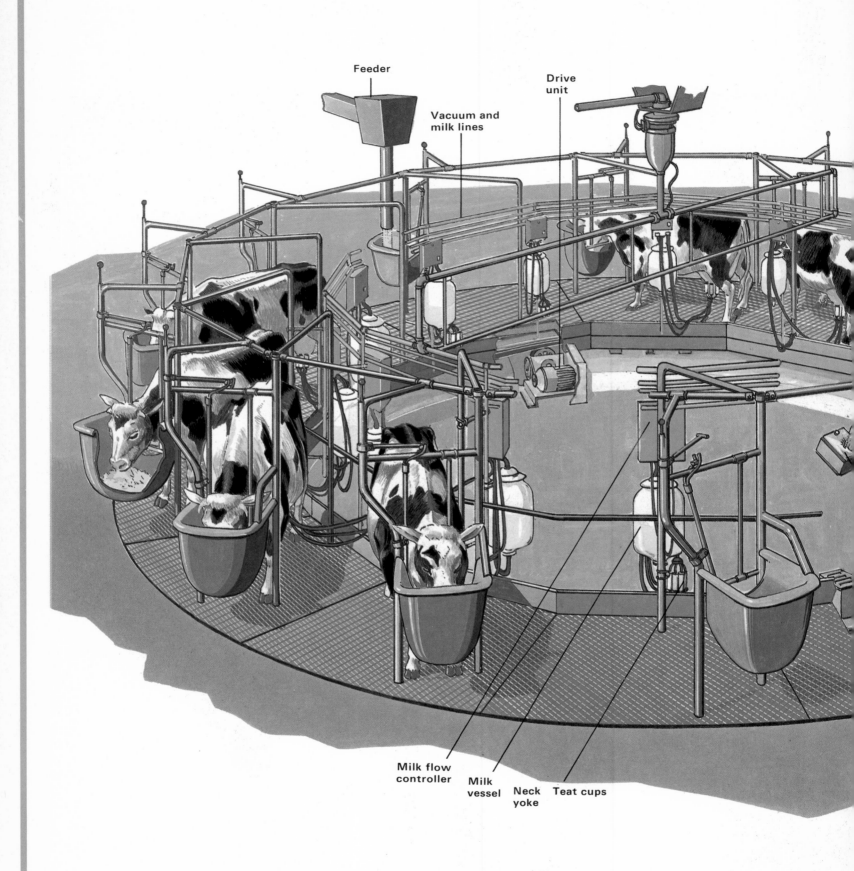

Feeder

Drive unit

Vacuum and milk lines

Milk flow controller

Milk vessel

Neck yoke

Teat cups

Mechanical milkmaid: MILKING PARLOUR

Long gone are the days when a cowman had to milk each of his cows by hand, squeezing and pulling the teats to deliver the milk into the bucket. Now, milking parlours attend to the cows automatically, leaving the cowman free to marshal a whole herd of cows into and out of the milking machines instead of dealing with them individually. The machines milk the cows quickly and hygienically, saving labour costs.

Each cow enters a stall where stainless-steel teat cups with rubber or plastic liners are placed over the teats. The cups are vacuum-operated, sucking the milk from the cow. Pumps then deliver the milk to transparent interceptor vessels so that it can be examined before it goes to milk tanks or churns. The parlour stalls are designed to hold each cow gently as it is milked and to provide it with food during the milking. The machines do not overmilk the cow; milking stops as the flow falls, and the teats are then automatically massaged before the cups drop gently away, ensuring that the udder stays healthy and in good condition. Valves in the milk line stop the cups working if they should fall off accidentally, preventing dirt entering the milk.

After milking, each cow is led from the dairy back to its shed or pasture. The milking parlour is designed so that it can be washed out easily, and automatic washing units clean out the pipes and vessels.

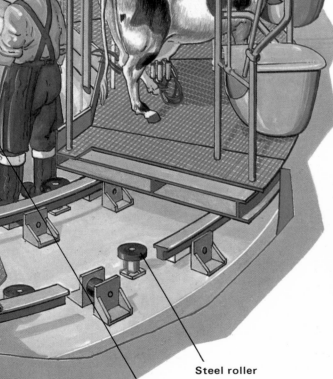

Steel roller

Control panel

As each cow enters a rotary parlour, it steps into a stall mounted on a platform that slowly rotates. The cow is fed and milked as it moves round, and it leaves at the same point as it enters the parlour. The cowman operates the controls at the centre of the parlour, but is free to move about and attend to individual cows whenever necessary.

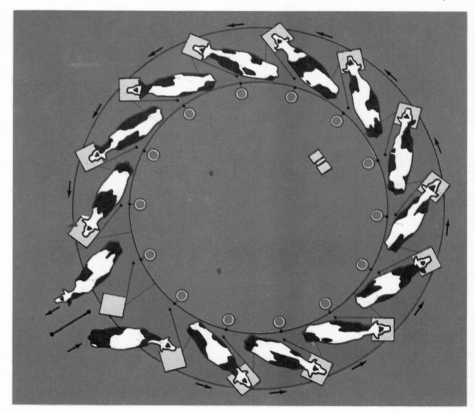

An eye for space: TELESCOPE

Since the early 1600s when Galileo first examined the night sky through his simple telescope, men have probed the darkness to peer at the stars. Larger and more complex telescopes have carried their gaze further into space.

When the Hale telescope was assembled on Mount Palomar in the USA in 1947, new details of the heavens were seen. Twenty years planning and construction and six-and-a-half million dollars went into the telescope that carried man's sight several billion light years beyond his own planet—a light year is 6,000,000,000,000 miles or 9,500,000,000,000 kilometres. The clarity of the image produced by the telescope depends on the amount of light it can gather in from those immense distances. The 200 inch (108cm) mirror of the Hale telescope collects 360,000 times more light than the human eye, and its situation 5,660 feet (1 725 metres) above sea-level ensures a clear view of the stars through air that is uncontaminated by dust and smoke.

A great optical telescope gives an astronomer an opportunity of examining stars directly or making a film record of a sector of the heavens. Most of their time astronomers use film records of stars and their movements rather than spending hour after hour peering through the eyepiece. The instrument's performance is judged by its magnifying power and its capacity to resolve the image clearly. So the modern telescope may be thought of as a gigantic camera with an enormous telephoto lens.

The light from the stars is passed through filters to take away all but one colour of the rainbow colours that make up white light. This remaining light passes through a photometer which measures the brilliance of the star that is being examined. An observatory includes a spectrograph that separates a star's light into its constituent colours. When the astronomer examines these bands of colour he can use the data to determine the composition, speed and direction of the star.

1　Lift to the prime focus cage

2　Observer at the prime focus point

3　Three eliptical convex mirrors

4　Dome

5　Oil bearing for the smooth operation of the telescope yoke mounting

6　Hollow bearing for the declination axis

7　Baffle for the cassegrain focus

8　Motorized wheels on which the dome turns

9　A focus for a spectroscope using a mirror above 7 to reflect to 9

10　200-inch mirror with an aluminised surface

11　Vacuum chamber for re-aluminising the mirror

12　Movable collar for carrying the tertiary mirror used in observing in high latitudes

13　Lower yoke bearing

14　Motor drive for turning the mirror to keep it aligned with the area being observed as the Earth turns

15　Lift for the mirror, used when the mirror is re-aluminised

16　Coudé focus

17　Main control console

18　Concrete pier penetrating below the frost line for total stability

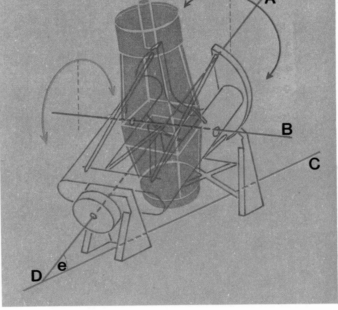

D-A is the main axis, pointing through the Pole Star

B is the declenation axis which rolls around D-A when observing. D-C points along the Earth's axis

The angle at e brings the D-A axis parallel to the Earth's axis

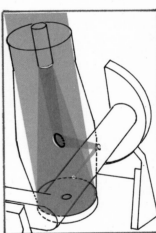

Focus through the declination axis

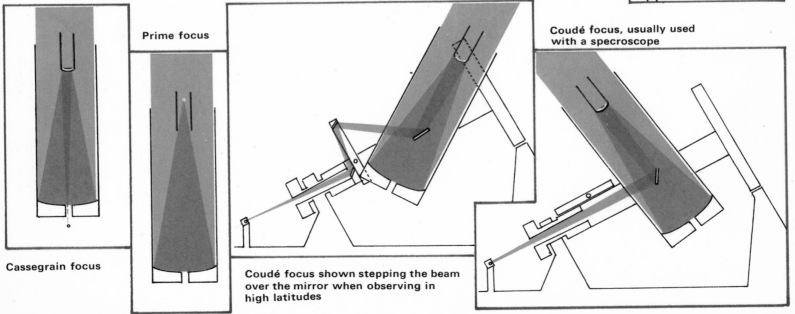

Cassegrain focus

Prime focus

Coudé focus shown stepping the beam over the mirror when observing in high latitudes

Coudé focus, usually used with a specroscope

Seaman's beacon: OFF-SHORE LIGHTHOUSE

There are few challenges to engineering skill greater than those afforded by the elements when men build a lighthouse out at sea. The rock on which they build may be uncovered for only a short period at low tide, so the builders must work fast to anchor the core of the lighthouse to the base rock. While the Inchcape Rock lighthouse was being built, the seas swept away shaped stones of up to two tons. The builders held the structure together by dovetailing the stones and securing them with special pegs, called trenails. The base of one of these great off-shore lighthouses may be 44 feet (13·4 metres) in diameter and about 17 feet (4·8 metres) high. The core rises for a further 22 feet (6·6 metres) or so of stone, solid except for a fresh water tank let into its upper section. The tower may soar to more than 120 feet (33·45 metres) altogether, a mass of about 4,600 tons of stone, resisting wind and waves, to raise the light high enough to be seen by sailors over the curve of the Earth at a safe distance from the hazard on which the lighthouse stands. Sailors can see a light placed 120 feet high at a range of about 12·56 miles (20km) in fairly clear weather.

An off-shore light is tended by a team of keepers, three on duty and a fourth on relief ashore. The strength of the light is chosen for the weather conditions it must penetrate. The lights may be of anything between 10,000 candlepower and over 1,000,000 candlepower. Weather can close in to make conditions where the light is useless, so modern lighthouses are fitted with powerful compressed-air fog signals. Some are also equipped with explosive signals, one type of which fires a four-ounce (280g), Tonite charge at intervals. Any sailor will hear this warning within four miles, even in poor weather.

Ground plans

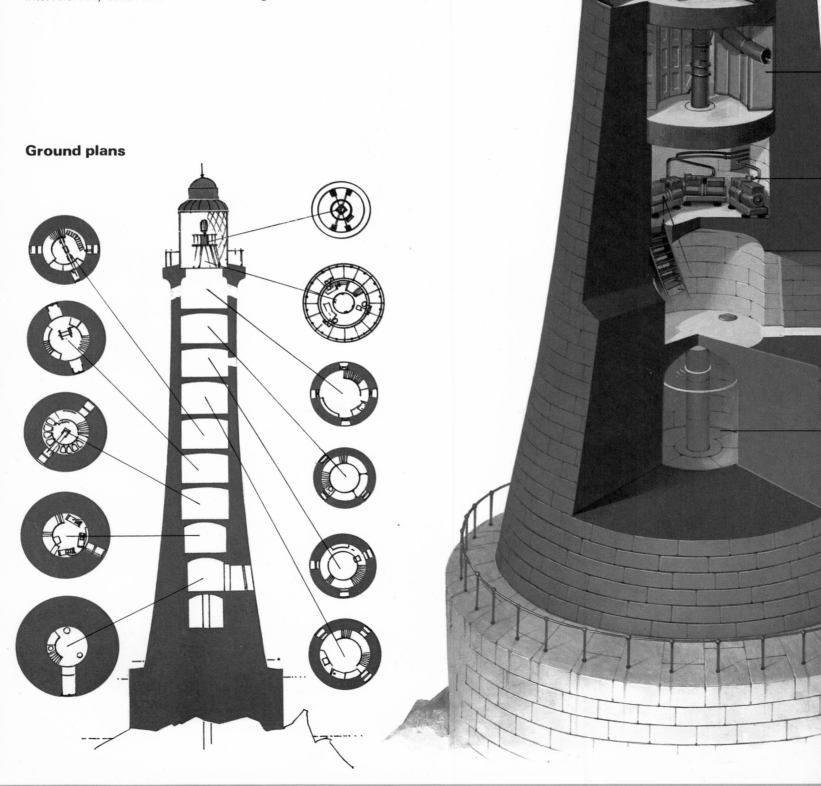

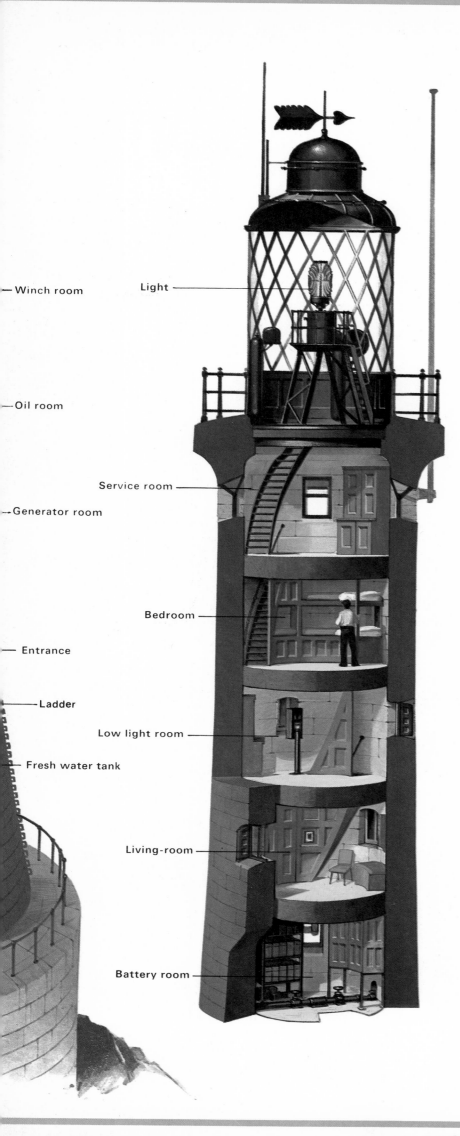

- Winch room
- Oil room
- Generator room
- Entrance
- Ladder
- Fresh water tank

Light
Service room

Bedroom

Low light room

Living-room

Battery room

The light

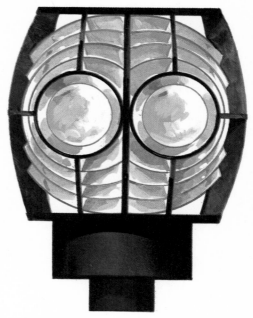

Many of the older lighthouses still use these beautifully made lights whose beams are concentrated as they pass through glass prisms. The whole light revolves smoothly in a bath of mercury, and is driven by an electric motor.

Another type of light consists of a mounting of two 1,000 watt bulbs, only one of which is used at a time. When one fails, the other automatically takes over the sequence of flashes, and a warning light goes on to alert the lighthouseman on watch. This failsafe system is taken as far as including two motors to revolve the light, and two stand-by generators to supply the power for the light itself.

Lake Maker: DAM

The principle of damming a river to control its flow in order to improve navigation or for irrigation has been understood for centuries. It is only in the last two centuries that men have used reservoirs and their dams for other purposes. As urban population grew in industrial nations during the last century, reservoirs for drinking water and for industrial uses became necessary. With the introduction of the turbine, hydro-electric power rose to a place of prominence in countries where the conditions for the harnessing of water power were present.

There are several kinds of dam. A *gravity dam* depends on a simple, thick, heavy bank of impervious material to hold back the water. An *arch dam* is rather like a large bridge laid on its side so that the pressure of the water is transmitted to the ends of the arch, which are sunk deep into the walls of a rocky gorge. A *cupola dam's* wall arches like that of an arch dam and curves vertically as well for great strength. The pre-stressed vertical *cantilever dam* is keyed deep into bedrock, and gains its strength from vertical steel piles clothed in concrete. On this page is a *butress dam*, which has a long straight wall faced with impervious rock round a core of compacted clay and concrete.

Water flows at high pressure through the penstocks, and spins the turbines which turn generator rotors. The power produced is increased in the transformers and goes to sub-stations to supply the National Grid and other consumers. The water rushes on into the tail race below the dam.

Sluice lifting machinery

Reservoir

Sluice gate

Filter for debris

Penstock

Sluice control building

Roadway crossing the dam

Penstocks

Cables for carrying electricity to sub-stations.

Generators

Transformers

Spillway for excess water

Tail water

Generator control room

Excitor motor for the magnetic poles of the generator

Switch gear

Cables supplying 110,000 volts to the National Grid

Transformers

Fixed stator conductor

Generator rotor

Turbine blades

Sluice gate releasing tail water to the race

BUILDING FOR ENTERTAINMENT

Carousel

Today we are used to the idea of seeing elaborate buildings created to house our entertainments; but in the past, when the simplest demands of living placed heavy pressures on human resources of time, energy and raw materials, they were rare. Entertainment in those early times was often interwoven with a people's rituals. The Ancient Greeks used to chant a poem called a dithyramb while dancing a circular figure. The dithyramb was gradually developed from a sacred poem into a form of drama that led to the fully fledged classical drama of the Greeks. By 500 BC, the Greeks were building theatres especially for these performances, which, in their early form had been played in market squares or any suitable central place.

The shape of the ancient theatre followed the needs of the circular dance from which the drama had grown. The orchestra — an acting and dancing area for the chorus, a body of players who commented on the actions of the main characters — remained circular. The principal actors stood on a raised stage in front of a wall pierced by three doorways. From the wall, in later times would hang a painted scene to act as a backcloth to the play. This scenery took its name from the Greek word for the wall from which it hung, the "skene".

The magnificent open air Greek amphitheatres were often built so that the audience faced the sea so that the setting was free from distraction. The acoustic properties of these bowl-shaped buildings are such that even a whisper, projected by a skillful actor, could be heard by the entire audience.

Theatres became more elaborate until the end of the Roman era. The stage extended forwards into the orchestra, which lost much of its importance. Roman entertainments included plays, mimes, concerts of music, dances, readings of books on history and contemporary events and circuses. The latter took their name from the circular arenas in which they were performed.

Nero's great circus, the Colosseum, still standing in Rome, saw many spectacular and some terrible events. While some of the entertainments were athletic contests or lavishly mounted plays and pageants, others were brutish excuses for the slaughter of gladiators, religious martyrs and wild beasts, revolting all but the most cruel and hardened spectators.

The Dark Ages that followed the fall of Rome and its empire brought a long break in the traditions of the theatre and circus. No nation had the resources to spend on large building operations for any purpose other than defence and worship. The plays of the Middle Ages were acted either in Church or carried about towns on carts, the players using them as temporary stages.

As courts became richer and more secure, spectacular pageants and plays were held in the homes of the wealthy nobles. Soon, in the great city states of fifteenth-century Italy, Florence, Milan and others, powerful families vied with one another in displays of arts and entertainments. Theatres on the late Roman model were built, and plays and lavish entertainments were staged.

The English had to wait until Elizabeth I's reign before they could go to a public theatre. The simple, circular building with its deep apron stage — emulating the Greek tradition — was the instrument of a sudden outburst of theatrical genius in the plays of William Shakespeare, the like of which has never been surpassed, even in much more elaborate theatres.

Unlike the Elizabethan theatres, later theatres were completely covered buildings, and most stages were set back from the audiences behind a frame called a proscenium arch. In this context, producers could mount spectacular shows with all the mechanics of scenery and lighting hidden behind the arch. This left the audience as spectators, looking at the play or opera through the frame, separate from the action on stage. In some modern theatres, there has been an attempt to revive the apron stage, which has the effect of increasing the players' contact with their audience.

Fairground entertainment has a history running back many centuries, and probably its oldest turn is the carousel. In the nineteenth century steam power replaced a good hefty push, while now a diesel engine swings the revellers round. The demands of the twentieth century require that many fairs are brought under cover, and the carousel is now found in large buildings at seaside resorts, out of wind and rain.

In many ways early cinemas owe much to the decorative styles of music halls with their red plush and gilt, circuses and fairs with their tradition of fantastic ornamentation. As films became popular in the 1920s, large cinemas of extravagant and bizarre design appeared. Visitors were ushered to their seats through marble halls surrounded with bas reliefs of exotic animals, plants and mythological figures, and as the lights went up in the interval they found themselves inside an ice palace or a grotto of stalactites or an art deco dream of the future.

There was a long gap in time between the arenas of the Ancient Greeks and the Romans and the sports stadiums of modern times, and in between there was very little. A few real tennis courts and indoor riding schools were built in the sixteenth century, but it was

Colosseum, Rome

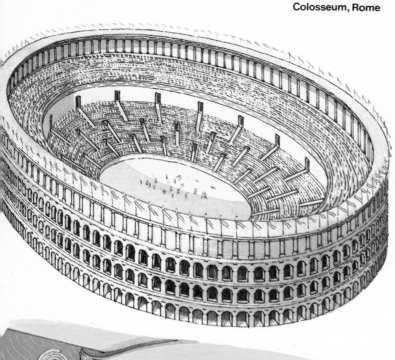

Elizabethan theatre

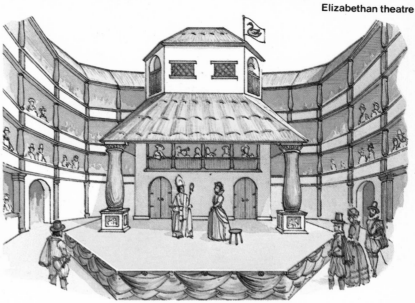

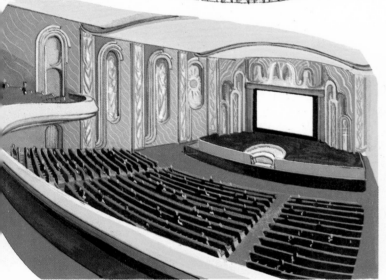

Cinema of the 1930 s

Royal Festival Hall, London

Eighteenth-century playhouse

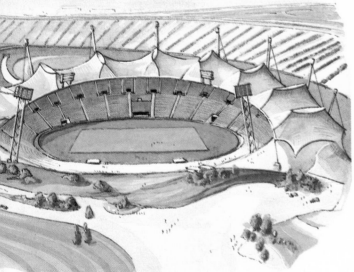

Olympic stadium, Munich

not until the present century that the great sports stadiums appeared. At first rough shelters for the crowd, they became grandiose weighty buildings surrounding a central arena or pitch and reflecting the nation's or club's desire for prestige. Since the 1940s, designers have tried to make their stadiums more fun. The Olympic stadium in Munich, with its light canopies and com-

fortable seating with uninterrupted views of the action is a fine example of the new type.

All architecture should, in a sense, intrigue the visitor's eyes and contribute to his enjoyment of his activity; but with building for entertainment, the architect has a freer hand usually and can delight people with buildings that are pleasure palaces.

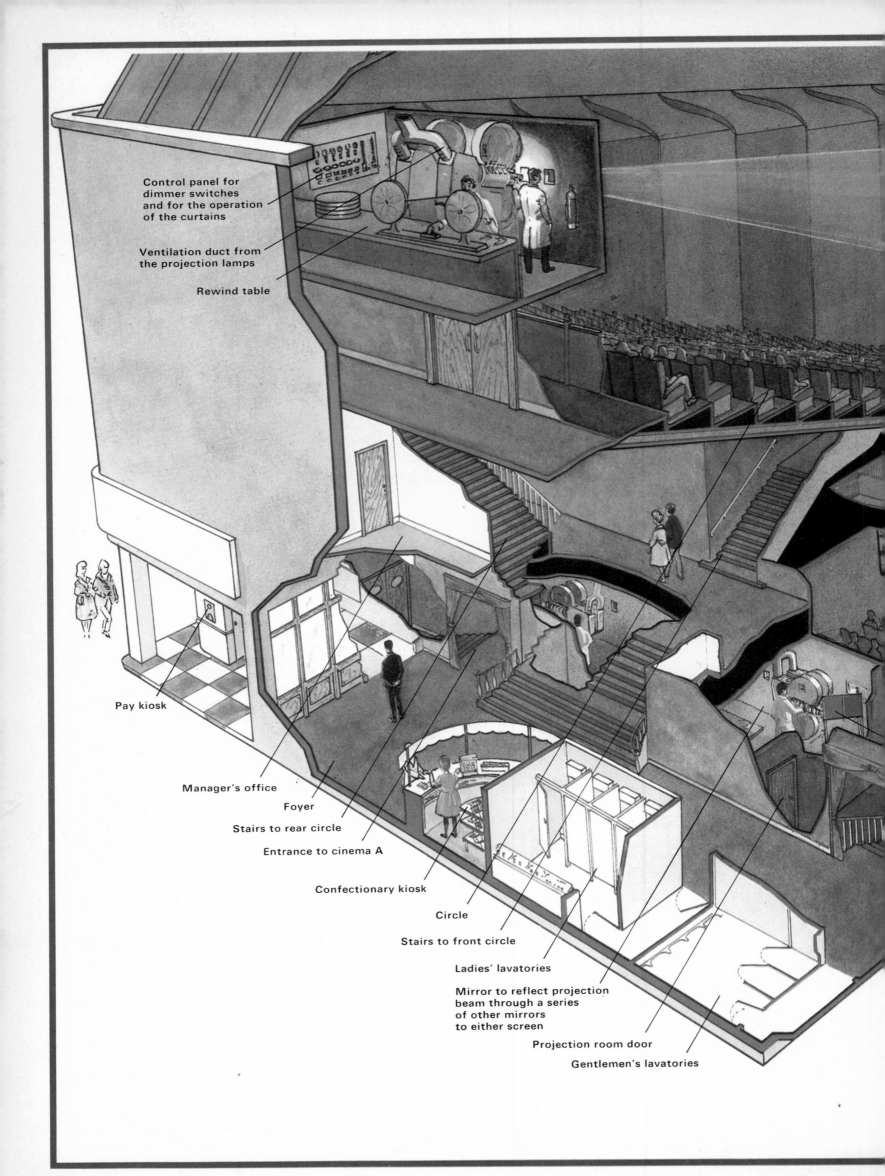

Control panel for
dimmer switches
and for the operation
of the curtains

Ventilation duct from
the projection lamps

Rewind table

Pay kiosk

Manager's office

Foyer

Stairs to rear circle

Entrance to cinema A

Confectionary kiosk

Circle

Stairs to front circle

Ladies' lavatories

Mirror to reflect projection
beam through a series
of other mirrors
to either screen

Projection room door

Gentlemen's lavatories

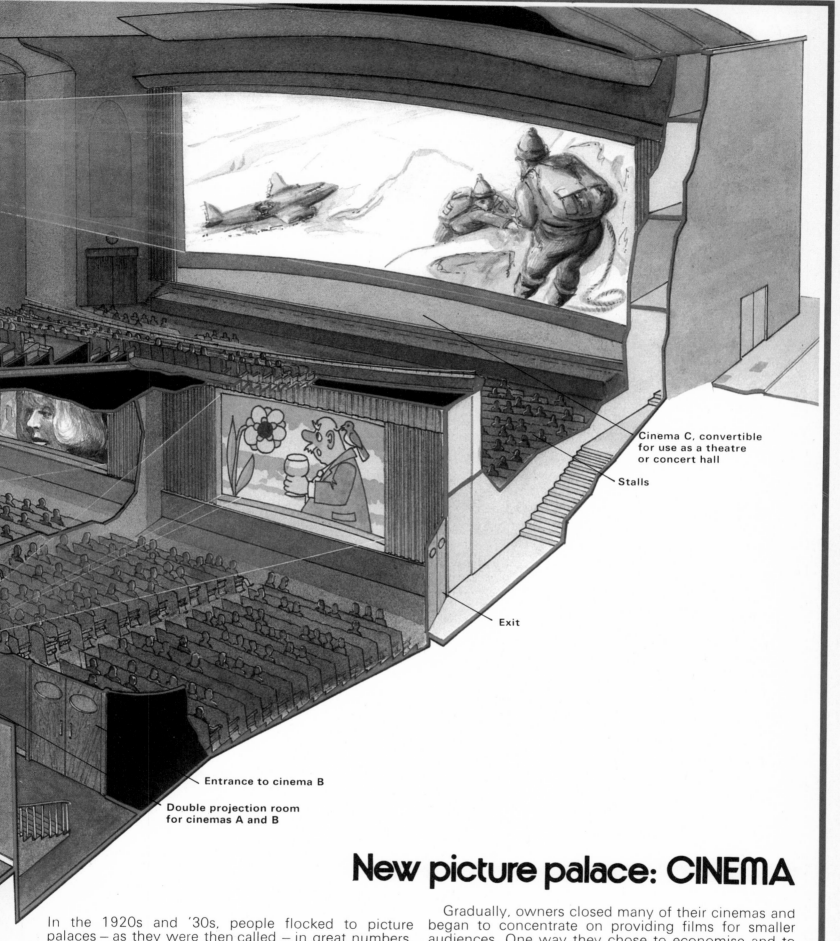

Cinema C, convertible
for use as a theatre
or concert hall

Stalls

Exit

Entrance to cinema B

Double projection room
for cinemas A and B

New picture palace: CINEMA

In the 1920s and '30s, people flocked to picture palaces – as they were then called – in great numbers. The owners of cinema chains built grandiose palaces for the enthusiastic public. The buildings were spacious, equipped with large foyers and restaurants, and were decorated with extravagant taste. Their designers gave them ceilings that were heavy with hanging decorations and walls covered with relief mouldings to give the audience the illusion of watching the films from the exotic surroundings of an Aladdin's cave. The huge cinemas of this period, seating more than 2,000 people, were hard hit by a reduction in their audiences when television became popular in the 1950s.

Gradually, owners closed many of their cinemas and began to concentrate on providing films for smaller audiences. One way they chose to economise and to meet the changed demand for films was to convert their large cinemas into two, three or even four smaller cinemas. This enabled them to attract larger audiences by showing films of a greater variety. At the same time, they cut some of their costs by continuing to use only one manager, box office clerk and the same number of usherettes. The costs of rent, repairs, heating and light were spread over the whole group of cinemas. Some of the most modern of these multiple cinemas can even run three films from one projection room, using systems of reflectors.

Entertaining millions: TELEVISION

Entering a television studio from a busy street, one is immediately struck by the silence. The walls and ceiling of the studio are lined with acoustic dampening materials so that sounds, other than those fed into the microphones which closely follow the actors and speakers, will not reverberate. The floor of the studio is completely level so that cameras can move about smoothly, without the picture jerking up and down. The set designer divides the floor space into *sets* of various kinds : a street scene, room interior, quiz game set, and probably others. Lighting of various kinds hangs from the ceiling booms and stands on the floor. Lights may even be attached to the cameras themselves.

The director controls events from a production control box that has a large window looking onto the studio. The control box may contain all the video, sound and engineering control systems or they may be housed in separate control rooms. The director has a talk-back microphone, enabling him to speak to the actors and floor staff over a loudspeaker during rehearsals. In performance, his instructions go directly to the headsets worn by his floor manager, his assistants and cameramen.

The producer sees all the cameras' views of his production at once on a row of monitor screens in the control room. From here, he chooses the pictures that are fed to the transmitters, mixing in video·material too if necessary. Where the production is a complex one, involving several cameras, video material and special effects that demand superimposing one camera view over another, he may need several assistants. In this situation, he acts as a sort of conductor, orchestrating the selection of pictures and the mixing of the video material, which his assistants perform to this timing.

Flood lights

Light, sound and mixer control panel

TV monitor sets

A corner of the Producer's control box

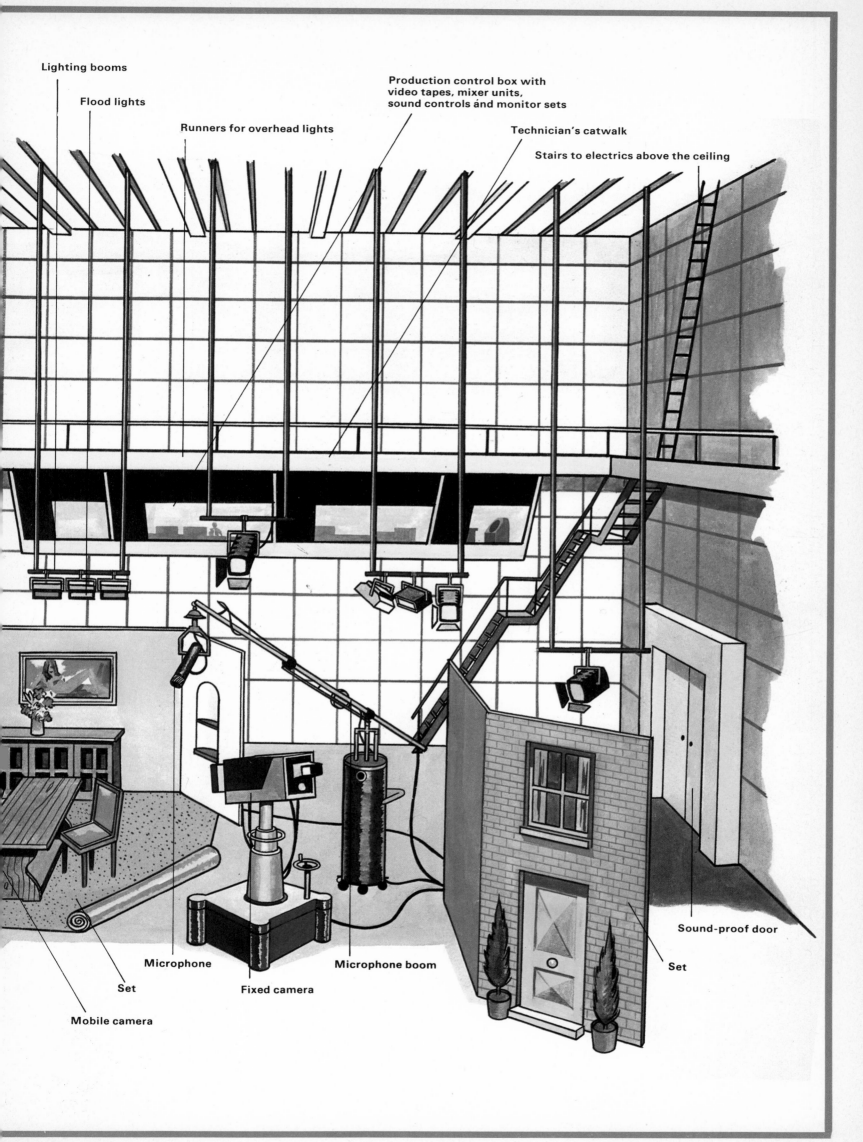

Lighting booms

Flood lights

Runners for overhead lights

Production control box with
video tapes, mixer units,
sound controls and monitor sets

Technician's catwalk

Stairs to electrics above the ceiling

Sound-proof door

Set

Microphone

Microphone boom

Fixed camera

Set

Mobile camera

49

Instrument for drama: THEATRE

The theatre today must be highly adaptable so that its managers can stage shows of various kinds, plays and music-dramas. In this theatre, designers have made a structure that can be set up as a conventional proscenium stage (picture-frame style) or as an open stage by lowering or raising panels from the ceiling.

The plan of the stage may be altered to make a large apron area projecting into the auditorium. Hydraulic jacks under the apron raise or lower sections of it to make an orchestral pit or to give the apron two levels. The cyclorama, to the rear of the stage is lowered from the flies and rolled into position along grooves. It is a smooth, curved screen on which coloured light may be played for effects, and which may be used as a screen for back projection of scenes.

Scenery is *flown* from the tower above the stage, and lowered into position when needed. This arrangement is far faster than setting up each scene afresh at ground level; stage hands have to move a minimum of heavy items, simply adjusting them when they are lowered to the stage and securing them with supports.

The lights on battens over the stage give a general light to the acting area. They are wired through a dimmer board so that the electrician may control the intensity of each group of lamps. The same is true of the front-of-house lights over the audience and the banks of flood lights in the wings (sides) of the stage. Spotlights, for lighting concentrated areas, may be independent of the lighting board and operated by an individual if the stage manager wishes.

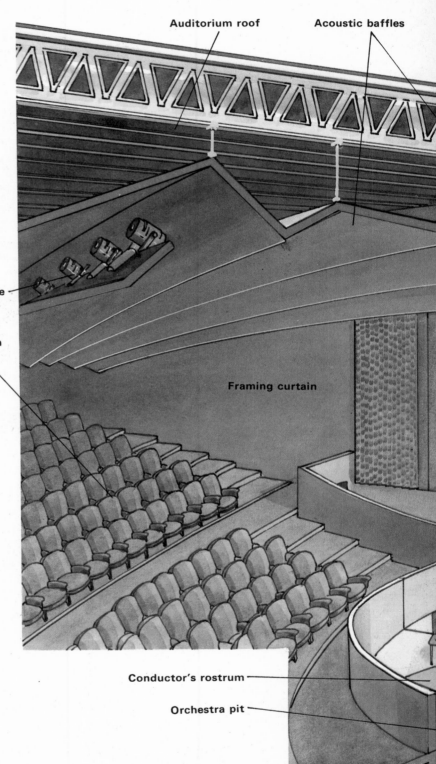

Auditorium roof **Acoustic baffles**

Front of house lights

Auditorium

Framing curtain

Conductor's rostrum

Orchestra pit

Hydraulic jacks for raising the front of the apron

Service door to the jacks

Trap lift

Dressing rooms

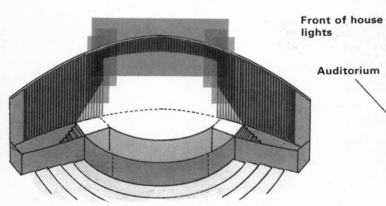

The front of the apron stage may be lowered to form an orchestra pit, and the close-in panels lowered to make a proscenium opening.

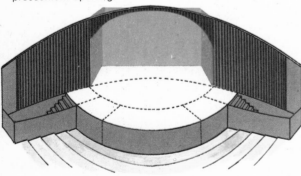

A full apron may be achieved by raising the front of the stage, but losing the orchestra pit.

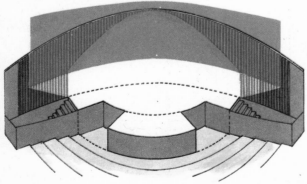

When the central section of the orchestra pit is raised, the actors have a small apron extension. Here, the cyclorama has been dropped in to give a background.

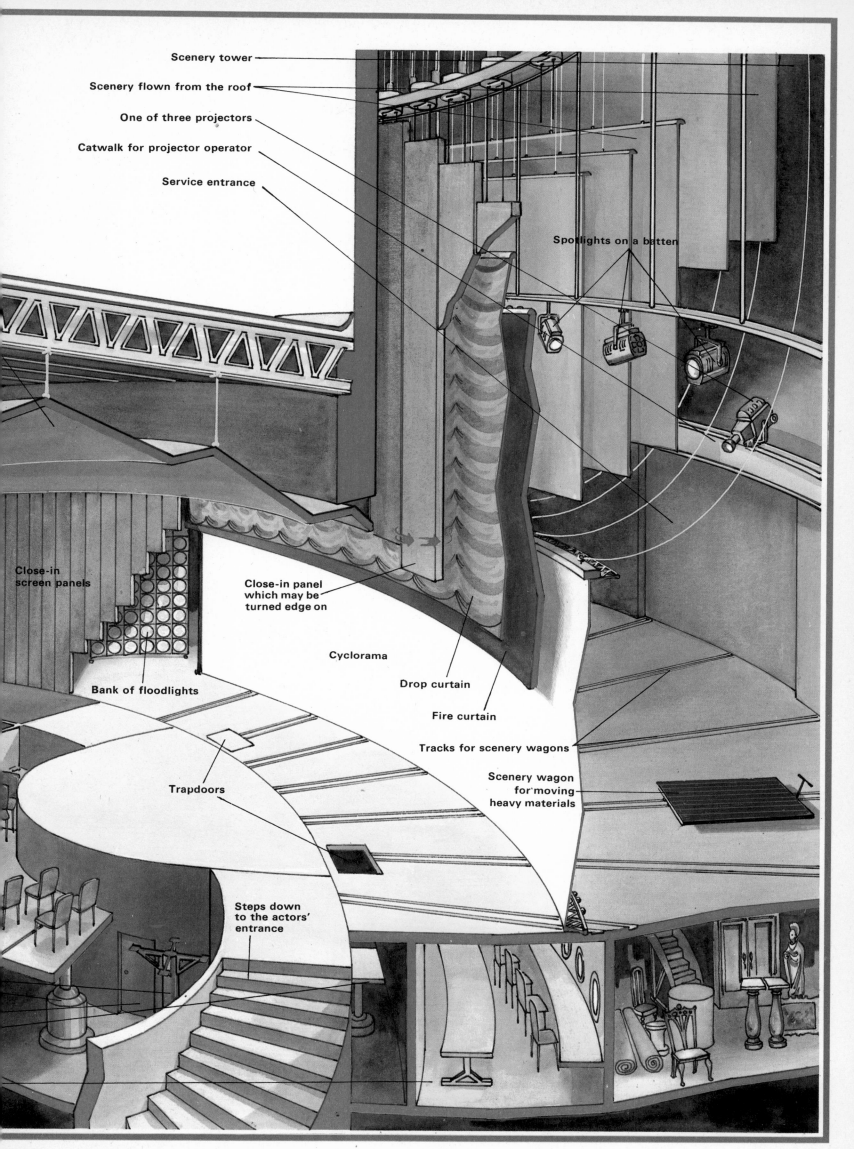

Scenery tower

Scenery flown from the roof

One of three projectors

Catwalk for projector operator

Service entrance

Spotlights on a batten

Close-in screen panels

Close-in panel which may be turned edge on

Cyclorama

Bank of floodlights

Drop curtain

Fire curtain

Tracks for scenery wagons

Trapdoors

Scenery wagon for moving heavy materials

Steps down to the actors' entrance

Parliamentary building

City strip

Geodesic dome

Megacity

BUILDING FOR THE SPACE AGE

The advance of new technology brings with it a demand for improved habitats. The pace of progress — in making new materials, finding new ways of working traditional ones, devising means of transport and methods of controling the environment — has 'taken off' in the last hundred years. Man has far outstripped the advances he made in previous centuries.

In the past, individuals or small groups have made attempts to impose a building plan on a new town, conceived and executed as a whole. The idea of building a planned city was an attractive one, but usually the plan broke down in practice because of the long period required to complete it. The planners could not anticipate all the changing needs of the population over a long period of time, or all the circumstances of their lives, so their plans frequently ran into a series of compromises that disintegrated into muddle. The much increased speed and mechanisation of modern building techniques make it possible to turn the plans into a city far more quickly than in the past.

Recent attempts to build planned cities, as opposed to those that have grown haphazardly, have produced such cities as Brasìlia in Brazil, and Chandigarh in North Punjab State, India. Both were conceived as state capitals, and planned to express the importance and grandeur of the state and its hopes. In some part, the planners of both cities have succeeded. Many of the buildings are extremely fine and their settings impressive, but they are curiously unsuccessful as places to live and work in. Outside Brasìlia, for example, there is a huge shanty town built by people who were attracted to the great new city by the promise of its buildings. They found that the city could not house them cheaply enough and could provide work for only a very few of the newcomers. The city builder's dream of inspired order can easily become a nightmare of chaos and hopelessness.

The need for modern industrialised societies to provide a habitat for huge groups of people has fired many architects to plan *megacities,* tremendous complexes that work towards an ideal of an integrated domestic and working environment for the industrial society of the future. To give the population swift access to natural parkland and countryside, some planners propose vast composite buildings covering a relatively small ground area, and providing for all that society's needs. This entails building extremely high, or excavating deep. The megacity would have within it all the

Marina city

Rocket hanger

Inflatable building

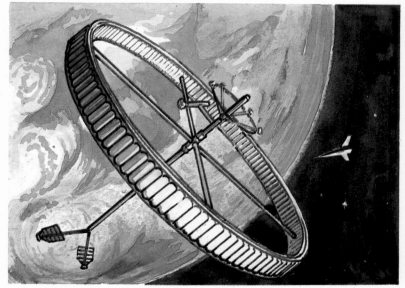

Space station

systems necessary for transport to its various levels and extremities, heating, air-conditioning and lighting systems, entertainments, working and domestic areas, leaving the surrounding areas free for agriculture and leisure pursuits.

Other planners, also concerned to retain all available land for agriculture, plan living and working areas over water. The Tokio Bay scheme is just one proposal of this kind. The buildings rise high over the water, and several parts of the complex are linked by multi-storied bridges that include transport ways, offices and living accommodation.

An underwater city, planned with the advice of Commander Cousteau, is yet another fascinating idea for a Space Age city, but the high helium content of the air breathed at depths makes food tasteless, speech sounds garbled, and its inhabitants would require lengthy periods in decompression chambers before returning to the surface. These disadvantages, and the loneliness experienced by people working for long periods at great depths, make the plan an unlikely one.

Many of the cities we live in today are over-populated and their systems overworked. Several ways of curing these problems have been tried : satellite towns collect parts of the population into new living centres ; ring roads carry through-traffic around the city centres ; and industrial complexes are separated from commercial and residential areas. But none of these responses to the pressures on the overflowing cities have proved entirely satisfactory.

Swiftly growing concentrations of populations in countries that are only now industrialising present a different problem. Technologists offer several possible solutions to the problem of providing quickly erected homes, factories, warehouses and public buildings. The more conventional methods of building with prefabricated sections and steel frameworks are supplemented by the use of geodesic domes for large and small buildings. Their triangular or pentagonal frames are covered with glass, plastics, sheet metal, wood or even cardboard pre-formed cladding. Inflatable structures can be erected quickly by pumping air into them, and they can be packed away again and re-inflated elsewhere. As temporary buildings, they are a useful idea.

The buildings required by space technology itself are designed with an especially close regard to their use. From this element of utility, a style has emerged that is appealing in itself, as can be seen in the soaring vertical lines of the Space Vehicle Assembly Building in Cape Kennedy.

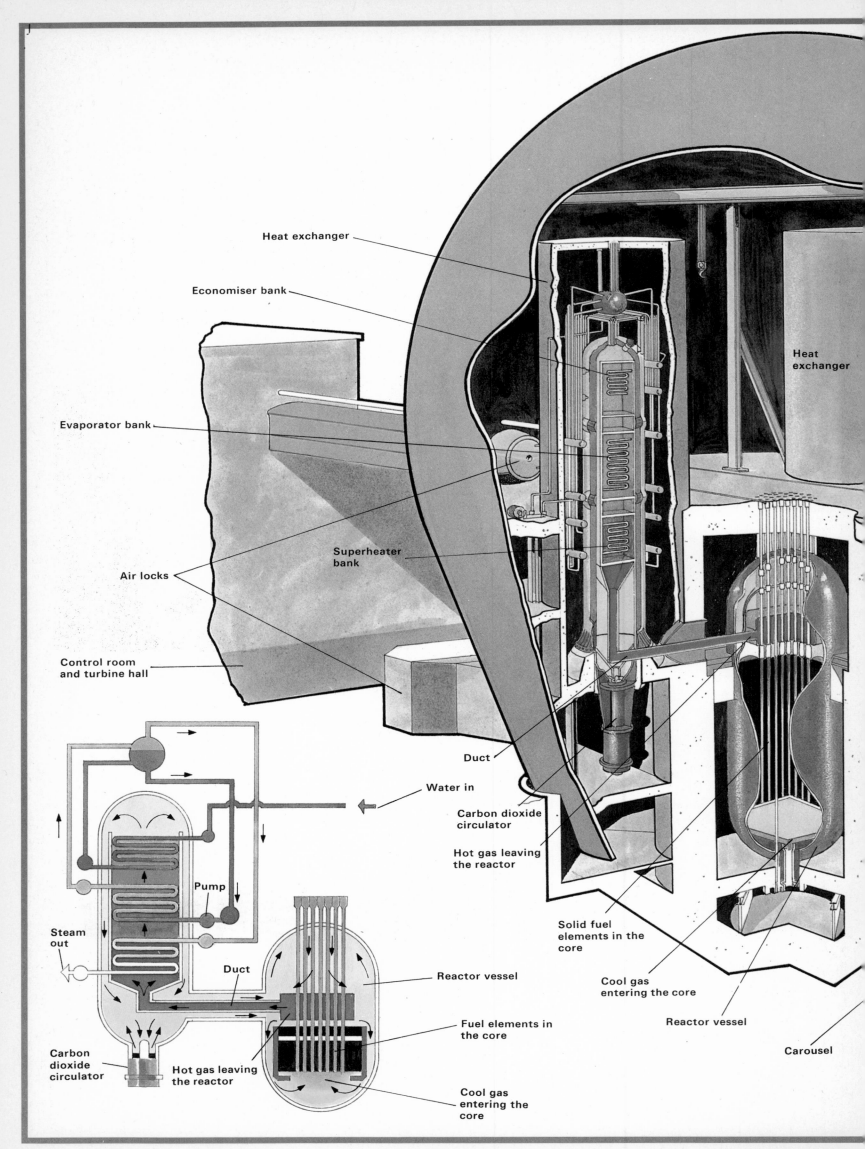

Heat exchanger

Economiser bank

Evaporator bank

Air locks

Control room
and turbine hall

Superheater
bank

Heat
exchanger

Duct

Water in

Carbon dioxide
circulator

Hot gas leaving
the reactor

Solid fuel
elements in the
core

Cool gas
entering the core

Reactor vessel

Carousel

Pump

Steam
out

Duct

Reactor vessel

Fuel elements in
the core

Carbon
dioxide
circulator

Hot gas leaving
the reactor

Cool gas
entering
the core

Power for today: NUCLEAR REACTOR

Though the wartime efforts of the nuclear physicists were directed towards building a bomb, they looked forward to the days of peace when the energy released by the fission, or splitting, of certain types of atom might be harnessed for man's good.

The first nuclear power station was opened in England in 1956. It was fuelled by rods of natural uranium metal, arranged in a regular pattern along holes through a huge block of graphite. The graphite – carbon – slowed the neutrons that kept the reaction going, and *control rods* of metal that absorbed neutrons could be moved in or out to control the reaction. Without such control the reactor could behave almost like a bomb. When properly adjusted the uranium rods merely became about as hot as an oven. The heat was carried away by carbon dioxide gas pumped past the hot rods and used to heat water boilers. Steam from the boilers then drove turbo-generators in the usual way.

Over the next ten years these natural-uranium gas-cooled reactors were made much more efficient by being made larger, with hotter gas circulating at higher pressure. The 1956 station needed three tons of uranium for every megawatt (MW) of electricity sent out, while the last of these stations needed only one ton. But by 1960 the first Advanced Gas-cooled Reactor (AGR – *illustrated*) was being built. This had fuel with a higher proportion of fissile atoms, arranged to run not at the 345-415 degress C of earlier stations, but at 575 degrees C. Each ton of uranium now generated 4 MW of electricity, and with temperatures rising to 800 degrees C the output rose beyond 5 MW.

In the United States even better results were obtained with the Pressurised Water Reactor (PWR) which used high-pressure water instead of gas and graphite. By 1975 British efforts were devoted to the Steam-Generating Heavy-Water Reactor (SGHWR), the first of which ran in 1967. This needs no heavy pressure vessel of thick steel or reinforced concrete; instead the fuel and cooling water are in bundles of tubes.

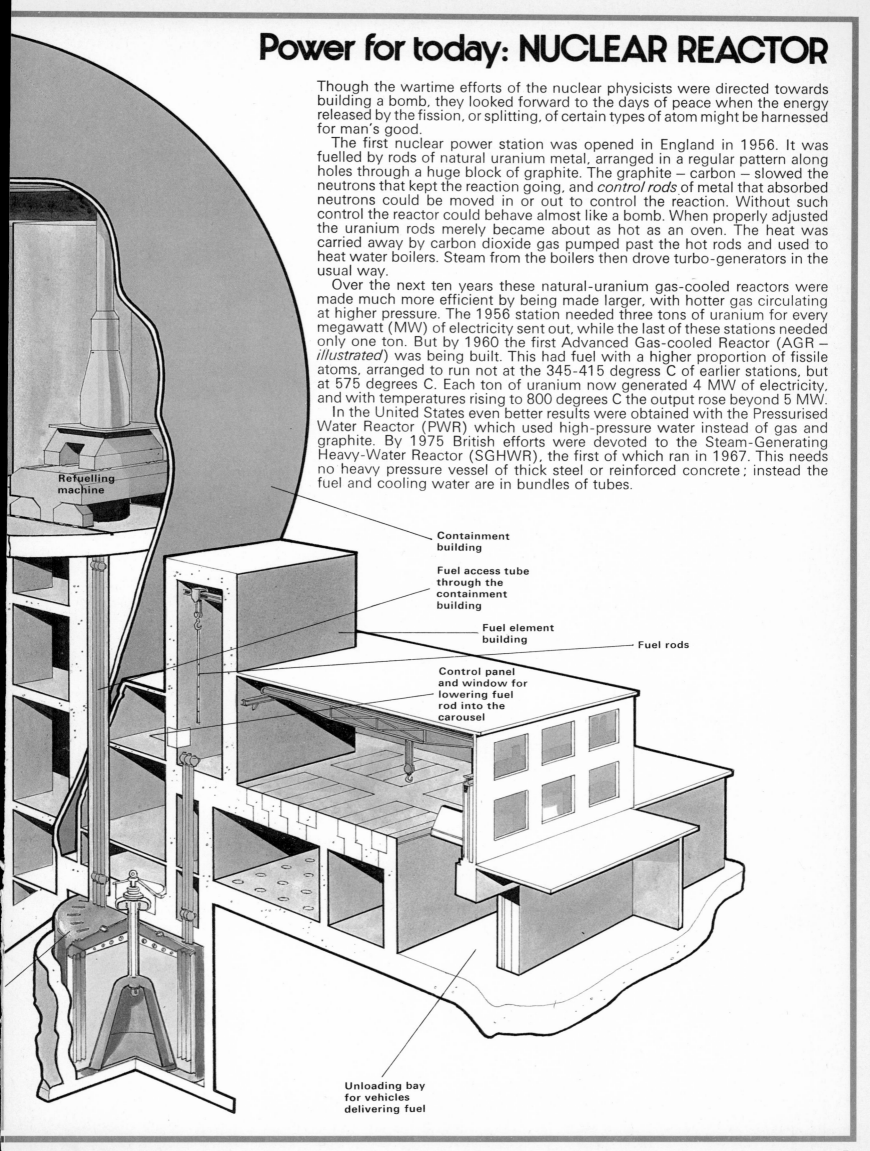

Refuelling machine

Containment building

Fuel access tube through the containment building

Fuel element building

Fuel rods

Control panel and window for lowering fuel rod into the carousel

Unloading bay for vehicles delivering fuel

Lift off: ROCKET LAUNCHING SITE

Rockets are launched into space from sites far away from towns and cities. There is a danger that they might explode or crash to earth soon after lift-off, and many rockets are sent on a course that takes them over the sea for this reason.

A launching complex contains several launching sites. A rocket is assembled elsewhere and then brought to the site on a trailer. It is then raised on the launching pad and attached to a gantry. The gantry supports the rocket and it also contains fuel lines through which fuel flows into the rocket's tanks. Some rockets have solid fuels and do not need to be fuelled in this way. A payload – a satellite, for example – is placed at the top of the rocket beneath a protective covering. The engine is at the base of the rocket.

The site team works for many days to prepare the rocket for launch. All its systems must be checked, and work may go on at night under the powerful lamps placed around the site. The rocket is fuelled shortly before departure. No-one is allowed to be at or near the site when the rocket fires. Apart from the danger of explosion, the noise of the engine is so loud that it would damage the ears. The team assembles in a launching room some distance from the site and watches the launch by television. As the countdown of time to the launch progresses, they check the behaviour of all the systems by means of monitoring detectors in the rocket. When only a few seconds are left, the engine fires and as it builds up power, the gantry supports move back and the rocket begins its journey into space.

We have lift-off.

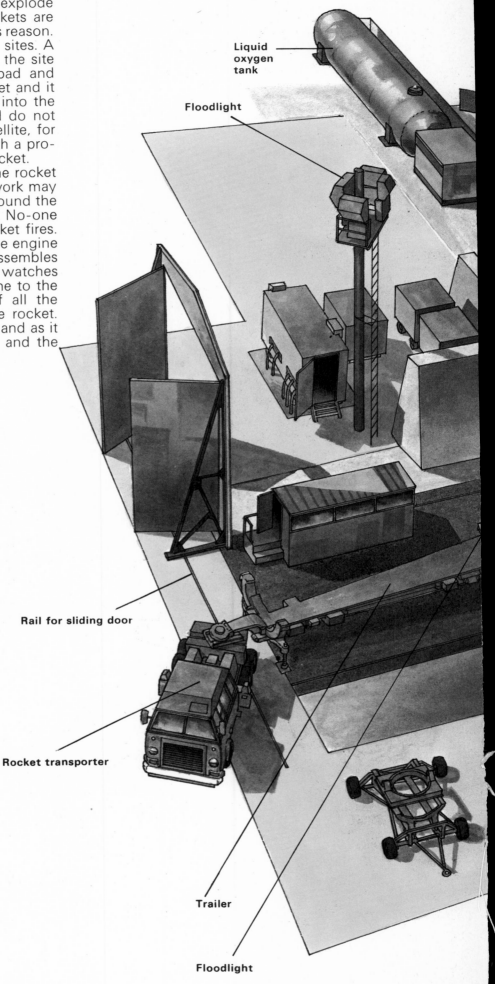

Liquid oxygen tank

Floodlight

Rail for sliding door

Rocket transporter

Trailer

Floodlight

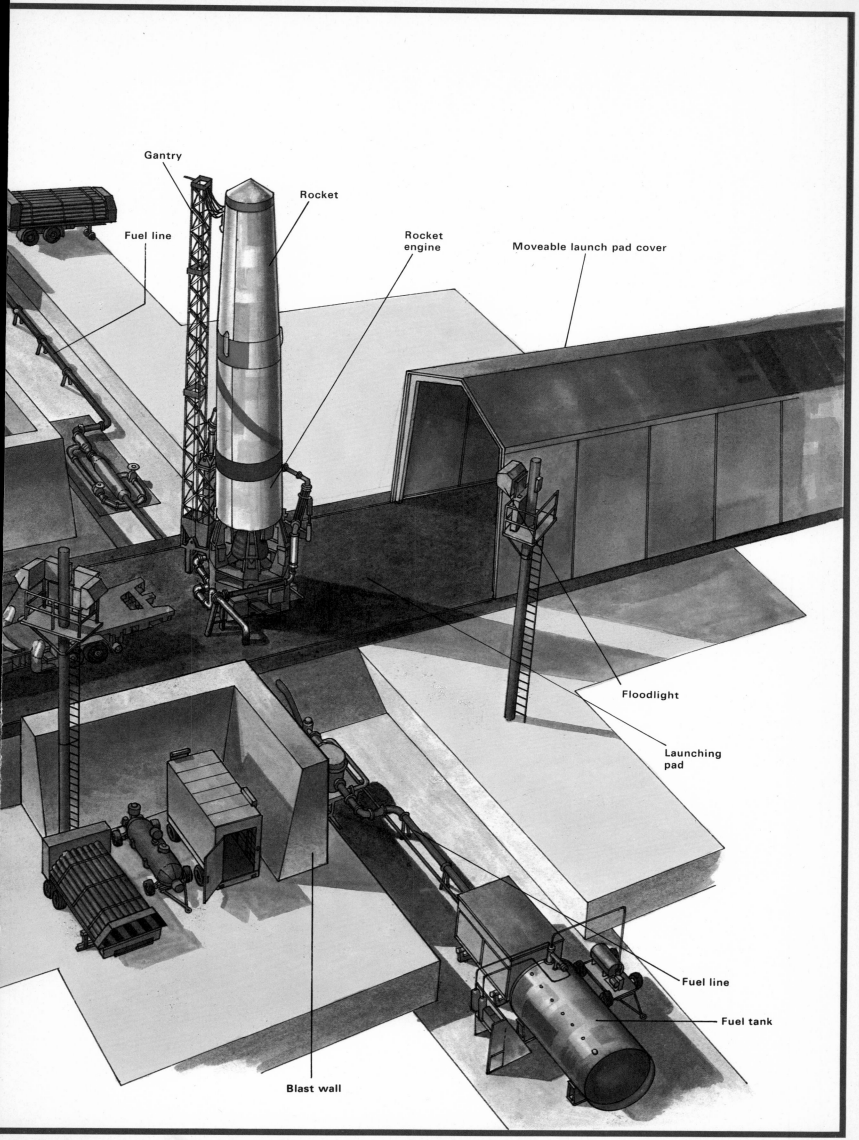

Gantry

Rocket

Fuel line

Rocket engine

Moveable launch pad cover

Floodlight

Launching pad

Fuel line

Fuel tank

Blast wall

57

Space-eye view: SPACE OBSERVATORY

Skylab was the name given to America's first space observatory. It was constructed from the large cylindrical third stage of a Saturn Moon rocket, but instead of fuel tanks it had living and working quarters for three astronauts. Skylab weighed 89 tons and was by far the heaviest spacecraft ever made. It was sent into orbit around the Earth in May 1973 and over the following ten months, three teams of astronauts visited it. The spacemen travelled to and from Skylab in an Apollo command module and spent several weeks aboard the observatory. Their work consisted of making thousands of observations of the sun and stars, especially X-ray observations, which can only be made in space because X-rays do not penetrate the Earth's atmosphere. Special observations were also made of the Earth below to survey large areas and detect natural resources there. Many experiments were also carried out aboard Skylab, many of them concerned with the effect of weightlessness on manufacturing and natural processes. One experiment was made with a spider to see if it could weave a web without gravity—it did.

The astronauts also had to contend with their own lack of weight. Their boots had projections that fitted into slots in the floor and walls to prevent them from floating about as they worked. Prolonged weightlessness also made them grow because their muscles stretched their bodies; the third Skylab crew spent a record 84 days in space and came back an inch taller. They soon shrank to their former size and there were no ill effects, showing that man will be able to make very long spaceflights in future.

Russia has orbited a similar kind of space observatory called Salyut.

Docking Adapter

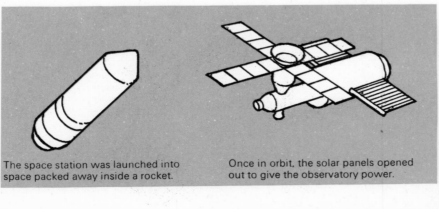

The space station was launched into space packed away inside a rocket.

Once in orbit, the solar panels opened out to give the observatory power.

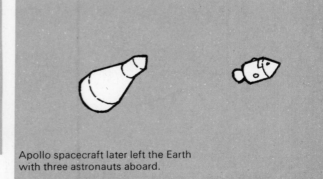

Apollo spacecraft later left the Earth with three astronauts aboard.

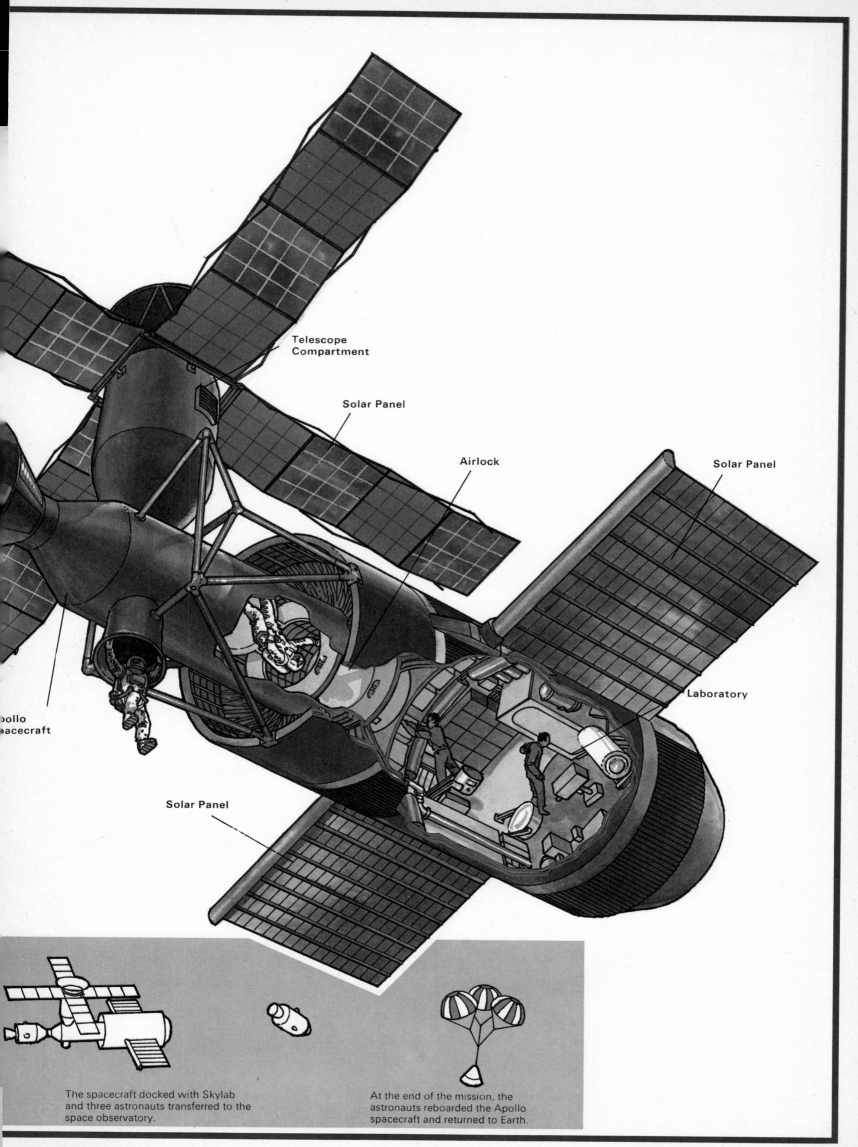

Telescope
Compartment

Solar Panel

Airlock

Solar Panel

Laboratory

Apollo
Spacecraft

Solar Panel

The spacecraft docked with Skylab
and three astronauts transferred to the
space observatory.

At the end of the mission, the
astronauts reboarded the Apollo
spacecraft and returned to Earth.

Long-range forecast: WEATHER SATELLITE

Satellites have revolutionized weather forecasting by providing meteorologists with a look at the world's weather at a glance. Orbiting high above the atmosphere, weather satellites look down from space and transmit television pictures of the world below to tracking stations on the ground. The pictures show clouds, ice-caps, and snow, as well as land and water. Weather satellites also detect the infra-red rays that come from the Earth, giving pictures of clouds at night as well as temperature measurements of the land, sea and air.

From all this information, meteorologists can see how different weather systems are developing around the world and make more accurate forecasts of the weather to come over large areas. The satellite pictures may also enable hurricanes to be spotted way out to sea some days before a ship or aircraft encounters them. The satellite's early warning gives people in the path of the hurricane more time to secure their homes, and get out of its way.

At present, most weather satellites are operated by the United States and do not give complete world coverage. In future, a world-wide network of weather satellites is to be set up by the United States, Russia, Europe and Japan. Some of these will be spaced equally round the world above the equator and survey the tropics, while others will occupy orbits that take them over the poles.

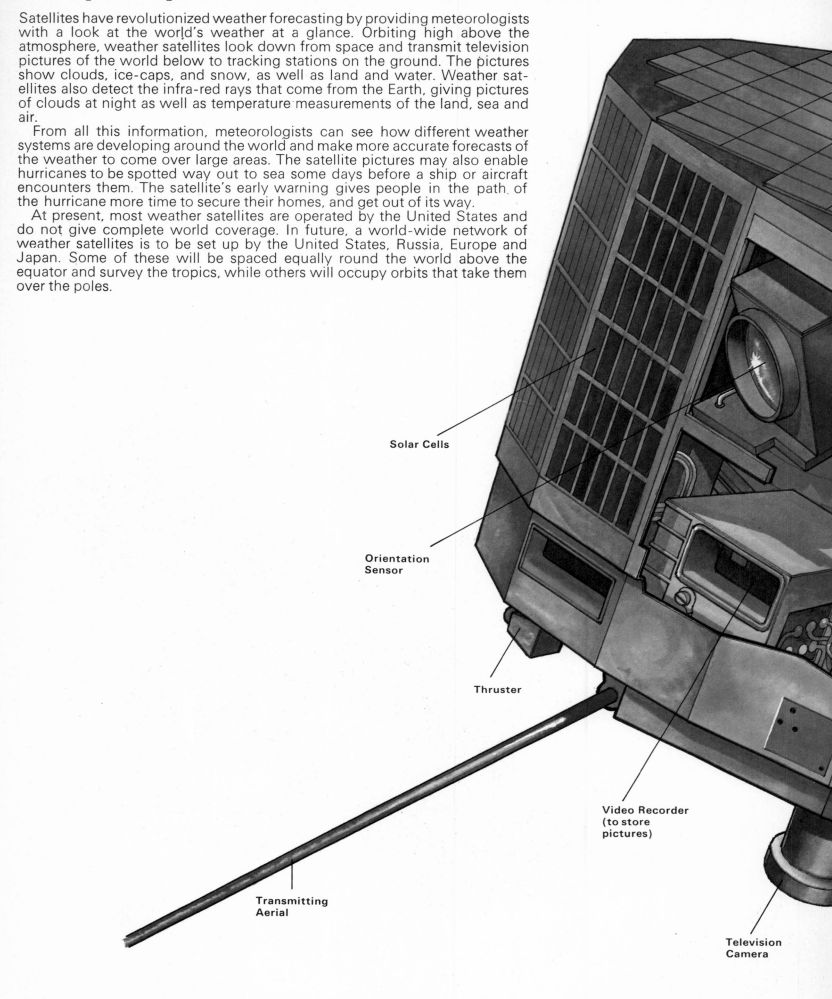

Solar Cells

Orientation Sensor

Thruster

Video Recorder (to store pictures)

Transmitting Aerial

Television Camera

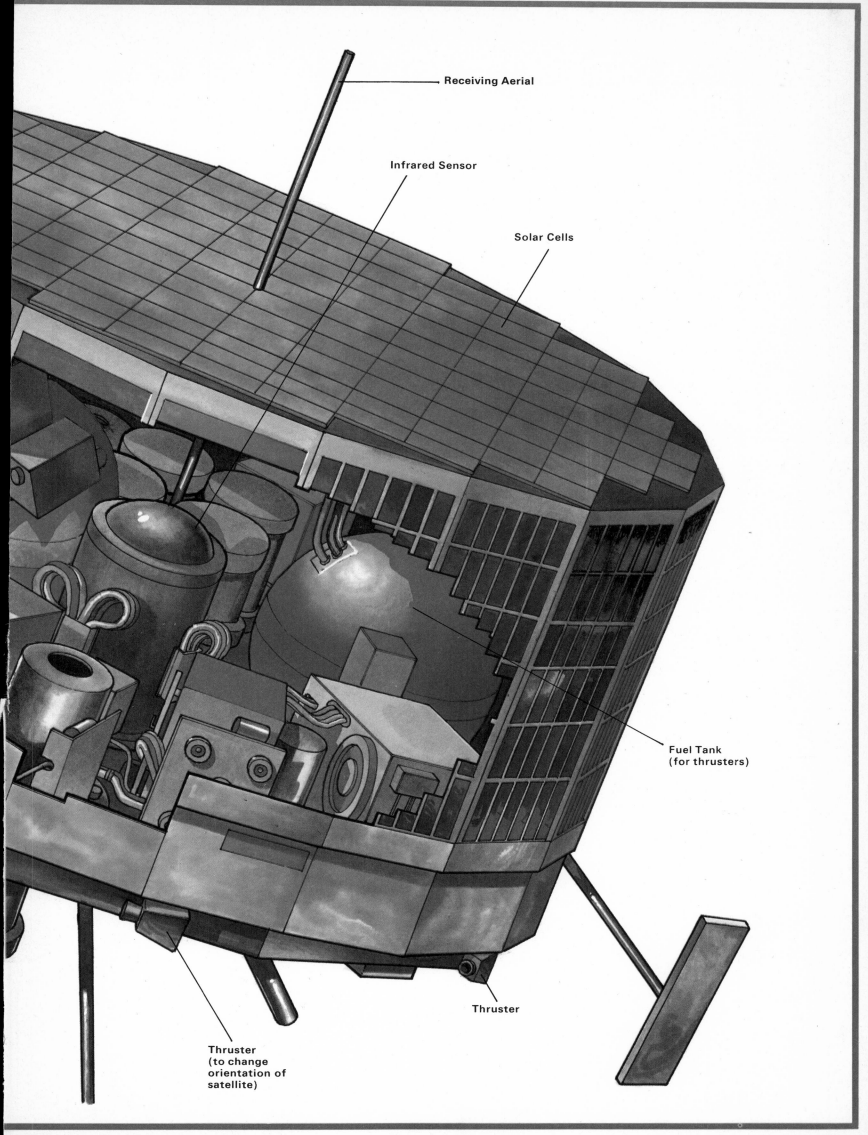

Receiving Aerial

Infrared Sensor

Solar Cells

Fuel Tank
(for thrusters)

Thruster

Thruster
(to change
orientation of
satellite)

Acknowledgement
The publisher and author gratefully
acknowledge the help received in advice
and other forms of generous aid that
supported them in the preparation of this
book. Of the many who helped, we would
especially like to thank: AGA Signals
Ltd; Mr Neil Ardley; the Atomic Energy
Authority, UK; British Petroleum;
the British Steel Corporation; Comite
National Suisse des Grandes Barages
Secretariat; London Airport; Rank
Leisure Services Ltd; Shell Centre; Trinity
House; and the Wellcome Foundation Ltd.

Designers

Al Rockall
Jackie Paynter
Veronica Gates
Malcolm Southward

Artists

Illustrated by: Ken Houghton, Brian
Lewis, Garry Long, Angus McBride,
Brian Price Thomas, Michael Tregenza,
through Linden Artists Limited.

ISBN 0 905015 02 9
PRINTED IN ITALY BY ISTITUTO ITALIANO D'ARTI GRAFICHE - BERGAMO

MOHN GORDON LTD. - LONDON